W
H
Y?

W
H
Y?

Glynis Baxter

The Book Guild Ltd

First published in Great Britain in 2018 by
The Book Guild Ltd
9 Priory Business Park
Wistow Road, Kibworth
Leicestershire, LE8 0RX
Freephone: 0800 999 2982
www.bookguild.co.uk
Email: info@bookguild.co.uk
Twitter: @bookguild

Typeset in Garamond

Printed and bound in Great Britain by CPI Group (UK) Ltd, Croydon, CR0 4YY

ISBN 978 1912083 435

British Library Cataloguing in Publication Data.
A catalogue record for this book is available from the British Library.

Dedicated to
Ian Baxter. My husband. My world. My inspiration.

Prolegomenon

A new life, a new spirit, a new beginning. Should be something to embrace, to celebrate and rejoice in.

Not to take for granted, abuse, spoil or control.

People always ponder on which is the greatest, is it nature over nurture, or nurture over nature. Or does a being, a soul have its own imprint before it enters the world, and no matter what, that can't be changed or controlled by outside forces.

People can become desensitised by witnessing horrific events, or working in certain professions; ie, fireman at the tragic loss of children etc. Does this stop them being human, or is it a shield to allow them to continue with their everyday professions.

This story will test these theories, as a child with no control is lead down a path of events by a controlling, vindictive, spiteful parent. Who only cares about themselves and not about the outcome on the people they are meant to protect or care about.

Was it their bad choices or circumstances out of their control.

What will be the outcome, who knows...

\

"Robbie, phone, it's your Mrs."

"Cheers Billy, I'm coming."

This was becoming a bit of the norm, and I was getting sick of it. We had moved down here two years ago, to be honest we had no choice the mining industry had dried up in the north and if I wanted to continue in the same line of work we had to sacrifice leaving everything behind, our families, home etc., and make a fresh start.

The National Coal Board had made it an attractive offer: a full moving package. Included in this was the cost of the removal men, a van to settle us into a brand new Coal Board property. With all the mod cons an inside privy the lot, no more freezing in the winter, and late at night walking to the bottom of the garden to relieve oneself.

The new colliery had a good future, a life expectancy of forty years plus, which would easily see me out, and the perks of a good miners pension scheme that would secure a not wealthy but comfortable retirement.

So we took the plunge, did the tearful goodbyes to our families. I can't say friends as they had all moved with us as a miner your life revolves around the industry. This includes your social life, with the weekend at the miners welfare with your colleagues and their significant other halves.

Billy was my best mate, we had been to school together and knew everything about each other. We had got up to all the usual schoolboy pranks. Once leaving school we both went into the mine together at Hauxley. Billy also had been given the option to relocate. So when he said he was moving it had made it all the easier to have an allie and someone to lean on in the early days.

Moving in 1961 from a small fishing village Sea Houses in the north, to live in Clipstone in Nottinghamshire was pretty traumatic. I missed the sea air, the ocean, the sounds of the seagulls, even the smell of the sea air was embedded in my memory.

Clipstone, though it was not a big village by any stretch of the imagination, had your village green, rows of colliery houses which we all rented from the pit. The rent was insignificant and taken from our weekly wage, it included our electric which was supplied direct from the colliery, so once I got my pay packet it was ours to do with as we pleased. Plus as a perk of the job I got monthly deliveries of coal which were impossible to wade through, and was full to the rafters in the coal house and was spilling out onto the yard.

The house was a three bed semi detached on a nice street, there was a scullery, parlor and kitchen downstairs, and upstairs two double bedrooms, a single and fully fitted bathroom, a coal house plus a generous front and back garden. The house we had left was a typical two up two down terraced seaman's cottage, front door leading straight onto the pavement and a small backyard which incorporated the dreaded privy.

Laura my wife on the surface, had appeared to have settled in well. Obviously loved the new house and all its mod cons and was pleased people she knew had relocated too. Soon after we were settled in to the new house she had managed to secure a job at the village welfare, as a barmaid and loved the banter and getting the latest gossip from the punters.

We had been married four years so our marriage was strong and healthy, and Laura had been supportive regarding the move. The only thing that would make our marriage complete would be the birth of our first child. We had not used any form of contraceptive from the day of our marriage, though we had a healthy sex life for some reason the baby eluded us.

Finally after actually accepting we may be a childless couple, she broke the news. I was ecstatic, scared an emotional mess, until the news finally registered we were going to be parents. Laura didn't have an easy pregnancy, she was constantly hanging off the toilet bowl with her head down it vomiting. In the end she went to the doctors who prescribed Thalidomide the so called revolutionary drug of the '60s to cure morning sickness.

Thankfully, she was in contact with her mother on a regular basis via the local phone box. Her mother managed to persuade Laura to bin her prescription and drink a herbal concoction that seemed to take the edge of her condition. So on the 4th August 1963 Laura went into labour, the midwife was called at 5pm and arrived promptly on her bicycle and took charge. I took the usual towels and hot water up to our bedroom only to have the bedroom door slammed in my face. It left me with nothing to do but march up and down the landing like a queen's guard on duty, ringing my hands and muttering under my breath.

I could hear them talking and strangely enough laughing and joking. At 2am in the morning of the 5th I heard the slap and the howls of our new born. I wanted to rush in and see, but I waited patiently to be called in. Laura was sat up cradling a baby wrapped in a towel, she was red faced and sweaty her fringe stuck to her face as I approached she sleepily smiled and announced we had a healthy baby girl.

I felt my eyes fill I couldn't believe it I finally had it all, the loving wife, a new home a well paid job with a future, and now the child we had longed for. The midwife passed me a bundle covered in blood and told me to go outside and burn it. I stood there in a daze, looking at the bundle, not really taking it in. "It's the afterbirth; you need to get rid off it, burn it now in the bin." I looked at her blankly, looking for the words, but she didn't seem the sort to take any messing, so I followed her command to the letter carried the bundle to the small metal bin outside, stood back and watched the flames take hold. I glanced at my watch it was just after 2am and here I was stood in the middle of my garden doing the midwife's bidding.

Laura soon adapted into the perfect mother, she decided to work part time at the club, as she wanted to keep some of her independence and not get lonely with me working long hours down the pit. Danielle Margaret Foster, as we decided to call her was an easy going baby happy as long as she was dry and fed. We had no real sleepless nights until she started teething at around six months, her little red cheeks all red and swollen. Laura had got into the habit of dabbing whiskey onto her gums to help her settle.

When our shifts overlapped we had a young girl from over the road baby sit for a bit of extra pocket money. She had been reliable, trustworthy and dependable for the last eighteen months, but recently she had become lacksey daisy since catching the eye of a young local lad. She had been crying off, making excuses, or simply not turning up. Hence the phone calls to get home sharpish as she needed to get to the club.

Working down the pit was easygoing, and you had a laugh with the other guys you worked with. Some only did three days a week and called in sick the rest of the week and nothing was ever said. So when I went up the pit early it was not a problem, I just made my excuses and left, catching the first available paddy out of there.

Arriving home Laura would be finishing applying her make up, doing her hair, making herself presentable for work. She always looked stunning when she left and I was left with Danielle. It was the same story: she would be crying in her cot either because she needed feeding because she was sodden. I would pick her up and the smell of ammonia would hit me, and her rubbers and nappy would be virtually hanging down to her knees she was that wet. I would complain to Laura about the state of her and that she was getting sore but she would just brush it off, saying she was late for work. I would clean her up but I was no expert. The folding of the nappies was beyond me: faffing with the huge nappy pin, I was always worried I'd prick her so in the end it was on that loose, that if she wriggled to much or if I picked her up the chances were it would drop off.

Finally getting Danielle settled I turned in myself, setting the alarm for the early shift. The trill of the alarm blasting through the darkness woke me with a start. I instinctively turned to put my arm around Laura, but my arm fell flat onto the empty cold sheet. Searching for the lamp switch I flicked it on and sat up with a start, the bed was empty – my god, where was she? Was she alright? I frantically pulled on my work clothes and rushed downstairs, she wasn't there. It was 4.30am. Where could she possibly be? It made no sense. What was I going to do? The club she worked at closed at 11pm and by the time she closed down she would normally be back just after midnight. So it was no good calling them as they'd be shut.

Danielle began to cry. Entering her bedroom, I felt a sense of dread and panic. What was I going to do? I picked her up, and instantly felt her tears on my cheek and the warmth from her tiny body. Cradling her, I suddenly heard the front door open and it sounded like something heavy had fell over the step. Still carrying Danielle I went to the top of the stairs, there was her mother: her hair all over, disheveled to say the very least. As I went down the stairs the smell of the alcohol hit me, she was totally out of it. I helped her upstairs into bed, resettled Danielle and headed for work. All shift I couldn't stop worrying about what was happening back at home.

On my return Laura made her apologies and excuses saying it was a one-off. Sadly it wasn't; it became part of our daily pattern. She would call me out of work. Go supposedly to work, then not reappear till the early hours, she always had some reasonable excuse: took her longer to close down, a party went on late, manager kept her after hours, and so on and so on. Obviously I was getting suspicious, I was listening out at work to grasp the ends of any rumors but none came to light. So I decided today's the day, I would go to work as normal, fake illness and go home early and may be get to the bottom of whatever was happening.

As I approached the house it was in total darkness except for the landing light being on. I took the key from my pocket, my hand was shaking as I placed it in the lock and turned the key. The key wouldn't turn, I couldn't figure it out, but looking round I noticed the top kitchen window was ajar so I levered myself up and managed to get access through it.

All was quiet inside, I looked back towards the front

door to see the key had been left in that's why I could not open it. For a moment I wasn't sure if anyone was actually in, and was actually starting to feel relieved, when a figure appeared at the top of the stairs. "Shit, Robbie, what you doing here?" The panic was obvious as he fled back into our bedroom. I slowly went up, Laura was in bed with the covers up to her chin, and frantically retrieving his clothes off the bedroom floor was my so-called best mate Billy.

I saw red, grabbed him by his arm that he was frantically waving about, and marched him out onto the street. He was screaming at the top of his voice, "It's not how it seems, honest, it's all a misunderstanding." I raised my fist and hit him squarely on the chin, sending him crashing through the picket fence and falling backwards into the neighbor's garden.

I returned my focus back on to Laura. I was furious with her, with both of them. She was still under the covers looking at me like a rabbit caught in the headlights. "Robbie, I'm so sorry," she managed to mutter. I wasn't listening, I was packing. I was done with her, with all of them, with this whole sad situation.

2

When people ask you about your first memory, no matter who you are, you have to stop, ponder, reflect, and search the deepest crevices of your mind figuring out how far back you can recall.

A lot of mine I may have blanked out, but my earliest one would be, I am guessing, around two years old bouncing up and down in a cot. My mother was speaking to a man saying, "I don't know how she got out, one minute she was here, then she was gone."

The man wasn't looking at her, he was looking at me; he was older than my mum and wearing a tweed jacket and flat cap. "Well you better keep a better eye on her, and make sure it doesn't happen again." My mum carried on making her apologies and he left. The room seemed dark and hazy, and as they made their farewells, I had my arms over the side of the cot clinging on to a toy, possibly a teddy, I'm not to sure. Then the memory just fades away, I don't remember feeling anything recalling this memory I didn't feel happy, or sad it was just like recalling a dream from the night before.

My next memory is imprinted deeper in my mind, I'm guessing aged around four. A tune is being hummed really loudly by my mum and I'm undressing in the middle of the sitting room, throwing each item off over my head. I am spinning around and laughing, suddenly a voice hollows out, "Bloody hell, Laura, can't you control that brat. Look what the silly bitch as done now." He was pointing towards an open fire, an item of clothes had fell into the fire. "Get her out of my sight and put the bitch to bed." My mother never responded, simply took me by the hand and led me away.

He was the first significant male I can remember, who was a major influence in my life. He wasn't around much, but when he was, there were rules to follow. He was constantly chewing gum, there wasn't a point when he was not chewing the foul stuff. He was always smartly dressed, a wiry man around six foot tall. With ginger hair and an evenly trimmed mustache. I had learned to be terrified of him, he had taught me the boundaries and the consequences of stepping out of line.

When he came home from work, as a four-year-old I would rush up to him hoping to be noticed, or at least receive a few crumbs of recognition I existed. I would occasionally forget myself and reach out to him. Simply to be slapped down, "Don't touch me, never ever touch me. You're filthy, get off." I would feel myself drawing into myself. I didn't have the words to respond I just felt scared, lonely and intimidated.

The house was a two-up two-down terrace with a long garden on the back; the front opened up straight onto the pavement. It was run-down and in need of repair. We had no visitors to the house and family only visited on one occasion. There was no laughter in the place, it was soulless, and my mum never cuddled or told me I was special, pretty or that she loved me. As I didn't get the attention, or played with, I was mainly just ignored so I didn't miss it. After all you can't miss what you never had.

My mum was hardly ever around, she worked long hours at a public house. So I was left with a sitter or my dad, Jerry. I liked the sitter she was nice, my mum would drop me off in the mornings, on her way to work at the pub, then collect me when her afternoon shift had finished. There were three other children there and we were all similar ages so I enjoyed letting off some steam and playing with them. She had a golden retriever that was gorgeous, she would let us dress her up and do piggy backs on her as she was very tolerant. The sitter made proper children's meals – fish fingers and beans, burgers and chips etc – not like at home where I had to eat what I was given or go without. At four, being given liver and onions or faggots was not really going to entice the appetite of a child so I hardly ate at home, and as a consequence I was a small, skinny child, pale but never sickly.

I was with the sitter until there was an accident; it was such a pity as I loved going there. All four of us were playing in the garden, she had called us in for lunch, and after we had all settled down to watch the flower pot men on the television, halfway through the programme she sent us back into the garden so she could hoover up. I didn't follow the other children out, but hid in the kitchen. I found myself shut in the kitchen with the dog, who became agitated when the hoover was switched on in the sitting room. The door from the kitchen to the sitting room was closed so we were both trapped in the kitchen. The dog's whining was getting worse so I went over to her to simply pat her, but she immediately turned on me and sunk her teeth into my arm. I screamed, the door to the sitting room sprung open and there stood the stunned sitter. "Oh no, you were meant to be outside, are you OK?"

She picked me up, abandoning the hoover, and carried me to the sofa. I was still sobbing, and looking at my arm that had the mark of the dog's teeth on it, but had not broke the skin. She was rubbing the mark, humming softly and rocking me on her lap, when the door opened and my mum walked in. The sitter explained, apologised and reassured my mum that the dog had never ever bit someone before. Even though I was small, I felt guilty and partly responsible, I should have done as I was told, and followed the other children outside instead of being stubborn and hiding. My mum picked me up and placed me on her knee and instantly the tears stopped. She didn't touch me so I was basically straddled on her lap. She looked at the injury tutted under her breath. The sitter was still apologising, but my mum told her not to worry as I seemed OK and we left. I never went back again.

My mum decided it was time for me to go to school, so she enrolled me in the local school. There was no uniform at the school so you could go in normal clothes. My mum told me all about it, how I was a big girl now, was going to make new friends and would have a lovely teacher to take care of me. Holding my mum's hand we approached the school on my first day. It looked huge and the building was in two parts: infants one end and primary the other, with two different entrances to access both parts. There was a line of children patiently waiting for the door to open to go in. I scanned the line they were all stood there boys with their back packs on, and the girls all scrubbed up with their hair in bunches looking immaculate. I looked at my mum unsure whether to approach, but then the school door opened and the line of children filed into their specified class rooms. A lady was stood by the door; he took my hand and led me to a classroom. "Danielle, put your coat and bag on one of the pegs, and then come and join the other children."

The children were all sat crossed-legged on a large mat facing the teacher. She was calling their names and one by one they were responding. I found the other children in the class distant, and no one approached me. At playtimes and dinnertimes I stood quietly alone, watching the other children play skipping, ball or simply running around. As I watched I became overwhelmed and burst into tears; I was sobbing uncontrollably, clinging onto the railed fence that made up the perimeter of the school boundary. I didn't like it there, I didn't want to go home, but home wasn't nice either – but I was used to home, I wasn't used to this. Everyday for the whole term I stood there sobbing, watching the other children. No one ever approached me not even the dinner ladies, they all just left me in my sad little world.

Assembly took place in the church that was on the school grounds. We were all led in and sat quietly, waiting. After a few minutes a figure would appear to float in dressed in black and white. I managed to figure out who was under this bizarre outfit was female, she was wearing a black and white head covering and there was absolutely no sign of any hair. She was wearing what looked like an oversized black dress that reached to the floor there was no sign of any footwear, which is why she appeared to be floating as she entered the church and proceeded down the aisle. I would sit there in total awe at this figure taking our assembly not taking in one single word just gaping at her in total amazement. There was never a peep from any of the other children they were all totally transfixed on her. On the odd occasion she or one of the others dressed in these bizarre outfits would take our class, we would all sit there as quiet as mice, I don't know if we were all in awe, or just terrified of the strange sight before us.

The first school holiday, I woke up as normal, went downstairs but there was no one about. I was hungry. I sat at the dining room table and waited for someone to come to me, all the while conscious of the grumbling in my stomach. I peeked outside, I could see in the house opposite there was a family sat around a table laughing, while the mother was serving up breakfast. This made it worse I knew I was not allowed in their bedroom, I stood and listened for sounds of life outside the bedroom door, there was nothing. In the end I couldn't stand it any longer even though I knew it was wrong I went to explore the kitchen for remnants of food. I couldn't reach the top cupboards where the cereals were kept, I was to small. I checked the lower cabinets which contained nothing but cleaning products and a range of different alcohols. It felt like I had been left a long time, I opened the fridge there was nothing in there that a four year old could eat, except an open packet of cheese. I nervously took it out, shiftily looking around to ensure I wasn't seen. I felt like a thief, I snapped of the end of the cheese and ate it, replacing the block of cheese and silently closed the door after me. After what seemed an age my dad, Jerry, walked in with his paper; not acknowledging me, he sat himself down in a chair and silently read it from cover to cover.

The following day I woke up again no one was again in the house. This time I was not so anxious. I looked through the curtains to the house opposite. It appeared their parents weren't up yet, the eldest had managed to hurl herself up onto the kitchen worktop and was precariously trying to reach for the biscuit tin. After a few attempts she managed to grab it and get the lid off, and with biscuits stuffed in her mouth she passed the tin down to her younger sibling who was patiently waiting.

I wasn't as hungry as I had been yesterday, so I went back up to my room and got out a colouring book and started to entertain myself. After colouring in two or three pages I decided I needed something to eat, there were no biscuits in the house, we never had biscuits or sweets in. So again I approached the fridge like a thief in the night, anxiously looking around fearful I would be caught. I nervously opened the fridge and reached for the cheese, glancing back for a final time, there was my dad staring at me through the kitchen window. My heart stopped and I froze to the spot, as I heard his key in the lock I flew up to my room, I could hear his footsteps on the stairs as he approached my room and entered. He stood there and simply bent his finger beckoning me towards him. Trembling I stepped forward, in a flash he grabbed me by my lower legs, causing me to spin upside down in his grasp. He marched downstairs, adjusted his hold on me as my small ankles were in the grasp of his left hand – his hold was so tight it hurt. Smashing open the back door leading onto the yard, he flung open one of the outside doors and, with me still dangling upside down he lowered me head first into the ice cold water of the outside toilet. I could hear my chest pounding but I was too scared to scream, my nose filled up with water and I was wriggling violently in his grasp. He lifted me a few inches from the surface of the water and left me dangling there. I was conscious of the fact that any second he could plunge me under again. He lowered me lower towards the water and lifted me up and down in the toilet bowl like some evil assassin teasing his helpless victim. Finally he raised me up placed me on the floor, and I tearfully fled back to my room.

3

I never mentioned the event to my mum, she was hardly ever around so I simply shelved it in the back of my memory. I was told off by my mum though, told never to help myself to anything again especially cheese, as it was so expensive and it had made my dad cross. She told me I should have waited as he was coming back, and he would have sorted me out something on his return.

I tried to avoid my dad as much as I could, keeping out of his way whenever he was at home. Odd times he would amaze me. I would still greet him on his return from work, and on the very rare occasion he would say, "You want some sweets, young-en?" My dad leading, I would be skipping down the street after him feeling proud I was out with my dad if only for the short walk to the corner shop. He would tell me to wait outside the shop, and after a few minutes he would return and hand me a small white bag with a few sweets in. I would light up, feeling chuffed at being acknowledged and getting his attention, and skip ahead of him back up to the house with a lollipop sticking out of my mouth. As soon as we got back in, he would be straight back into his paper, but I was happy, I felt if just for a minute he cared.

As I was breaking up for the summer holidays, my mum informed me I was going to see my grandparents up north so I needed an early night, as we would be up first thing to catch the coach. My mum had packed a lovely lunch for the journey, and she was dressed up to the nines, and her hair looked like it had been newly permed. It was the first time I had been away and I was excited at going away with my mum and having her all to myself for the holidays.

We caught the coach first thing, and when we arrived up north it was dark. My mum flagged down a taxi, which pulled up outside a modern semi-detached property. My grandparents came straight out to meet us, my grandma was slightly shorter than my mum with the same short permed hair as her, and wearing glasses, she greeted us with the biggest grin ever asking us about our journey. My granddad was around the same height as my mum around 5ft 3inches, but he was thinning on top and was very slight of build.

We were ushered into the house, and as soon as we entered it felt warm and inviting. The smell of food was wafting through the house and a small dog came running up to greet us. Ignoring the adult conversation I was on all fours getting acquainted with my new best mate whether she wanted it or not. "That's Tanya, hinny, she's a corgi."

looking up from where I was kneeling and struggling to get a grasp of this strange accent replied, "Hinny? What's that?" Everyone laughed and my granddad replied, "That's you, hinny."

Dinner was served at a large table in the dining room. I couldn't believe my eyes: it was a full Sunday dinner and it was only Friday. After my grandma brought out dessert – homemade apple pie and custard – I ate till I nearly burst. After, I was dozing off on the sofa, so my mum showed me up to my room which was a pretty single room. On the bed was a small white teddy bear. My mum tucked me up tight into the bed, which had been preheated by a hot water bottle, and I snuggled down with my new bear friend.

The next morning my mum came into me and woke me first thing. "Danielle, I am going to have to leave you here for the six weeks holiday, I will be returning back home this morning, I have just come into say goodbye, but don't you worry I will be back for you before the new term starts." Rubbing my eyes I sat up in bed and looked at her in disbelieve, I didn't want her to go, I had been looking forward to having her all to myself, I didn't know these people. As if reading my mind, she continued, "Danielle, your grandparents live such a long way from us and they have been looking forward to seeing you. You don't want to hurt their feeling by saying you're coming back with me? They will take really good care of you, so don't worry, OK? you need to be a big girl."

The tears were welling up in my eyes and I couldn't speak, so I just nodded my response, kissing me on the top of the head she smiled and walked out the room closing the bedroom door softly after her. I was unable to get back to sleep so in the end I got up, put on the new dressing gown and slippers my mum bought me for the holiday and tiptoed down the stairs.

My mum and grandma were busy in the kitchen sorting out a packed lunch for my mum's return journey. I didn't want to look at my mum as I was cross with her. They were constantly chatting and it took them a moment to realise I was stood there clinging on for dear life to the teddy bear from my room. My grandma was the first to speak. "Morning, did you sleep well? Go and sit at the table and I will fetch you some breakfast." Not responding, I did as commanded, and waited patiently for her to bring my food through. Tanya had settled at the side of my chair; I felt like kicking her as I felt powerless and like I was on the verge of being abandoned. While I was eating my mum came into say her goodbyes, I refused to respond to her and never looked up from my breakfast.

There was no sign of my granddad, as he had gone to work at the local shipyard in Walker where they lived, so it was just my grandma and me, who was busying herself with her chores. I was pleased I never kicked the dog in frustration because, as it turned out, she became my best friend in the six weeks I was there. I spent hours with her, teaching her new tricks. My aunties would call in every morning to take her a walk and I would go with them to the local park, throwing the ball for Tanya. On the way home we would always go to the local shopping centre where they would treat me to a cornet of my choice as it turned out tootie fruity was my favorite.

Granddad always returned home at half past twelve from the shipyard and grandma had dinner ready; it was always a scrummy meal with a dessert to follow. While there, I had my sixth birthday, and my grandma baked. There was everything under the sun: scones, pastries, buns, a homemade birthday cake and it was all really nice. My aunties and grandparents were there and they made such a real fuss of me that I never even missed my mum. For the whole of the holiday I felt safe; I had started to gain a little weight and gained a few inches in height. At the end of the six weeks my mum came to collect me, and we traveled back on the coach.

I was dreading going back to the house and seeing my dad, but when entering the house a huge white dog came pounding up to me, nearly sending me flying off my feet. I looked at my mum, puzzled. "This is Theresa, she has come to live with us," I loved Theresa instantly, she was a Samoyed all white and fluffy without a nasty bone in her body. I confided in her, she comforted me when things were hard at home. I played with her, dressing her up in numerous ridiculous outfits and she allowed me to ride on her back. I would cuddle up to her nuzzling into her, fur and we would both drift peacefully off to sleep, she made me feel secure and safe. She was the only thing in my mad existence I could rely on.

The following school holiday, my mum had arranged a new sitter – a teenage girl – she was lots of fun. She played with me and Theresa endlessly, took me to the park and taught me how to use my imagination while playing with my toys. On the Saturday she called in to collect her baby sitting money, my mum was furious with her saying, "Cigarette cards have gone missing, and it had to be you that has done it. You aren't welcome anymore." The sitter was obviously taken aback by the allegation and refused all knowledge of the crime. She said she had called in to take me to the park and told me to get my coat. My mum told her I was going nowhere as my grandma was visiting from up north. The sitter left obviously upset at being accused, and losing a week's pay. I sat at the front window all day looking out for my grandma but she never arrived, when I asked about it she simply explained there had been some complication and they couldn't make it.

My mum and dad had started arguing, on the first morning of my return back to school my bedroom door flew open, startling me awake. Bleary-eyed I rolled over in bed to find my dad standing in my doorway completely naked. I had never seen anything like it; I threw the covers over my head too fearful to look. "Danielle, get out of that bed now and get dressed, god help you if I have to drag you out." I peeped over the top of the cover, wondering where my mum was, I could see her at the end of the corridor sat up in bed with the covers up to her chin, not making any effort to get herself up and come to my rescue or even chastise him in anyway. I slowly got up, fearful he may return at any moment, got my breakfast and left the house on my own to the sanctuary of my school for a few hours.

The arguing between them was getting worse, it was relentless. As my dad entered the house as usual, even though I was scared of him I would go over to him and say my usual "Hello Dad". After all, you never know this could be one of the days I got some sweets. "Danielle, he is NOT your dad. Stop calling him that, he doesn't like it. Call him Jerry, and get away from him." I was still looking up at my dad, as she was saying this he was instantly furious, "How dare you, you heartless bitch." He threw his work bag down and stormed out the house.

I was left stood in the middle of the sitting room trying to process this new information, so my dad wasn't my dad, how was this even possible? I knew from bitter experience not to question her about this new revelation, she made no effort to explain what had been said so I was left to ponder what all this meant,

The following morning there was no sign of my dad/ Jerry I didn't know what to think and I couldn't take it in. When I went downstairs Mum was busying herself making breakfast. As she turned around her face was black on one side and she had a huge bruise on her left eye. I stood wide-mouthed looking at her, she beckoned me to the table to get my breakfast, not commenting on her injuries at all. A few weeks later I asked my mum when she appeared calmer, what she meant by Jerry not being my dad. She calmly explained to me that Jerry was my step dad. I asked her, where my real dad was? and why I never saw him? Calmly and sincerely, she explained that my real dad was dead, that he had died when I was a baby, and that's why I could not remember him.

4

Things at home returned back to normal, and I still kept calling Jerry, "Dad". I did try not to, and over time it got easier, but at first I found it hard to adapt. My mum and Jerry were still arguing violently and the black eyes and bruises I woke up to on my mother, became a normal part of life. When things were difficult I would snuggle up to Theresa, crying into her coat, getting comfort from the warmth of her fur and body. She felt like my only friend in the world, and I would sit and chat to her confiding to her how I felt, and she would look back at me with her big brown eyes taking it all in, but not judging or dismissing my feelings.

My great aunts from Walker came to visit and stayed at ours for a week. It was lovely to see them, but I couldn't spend the week with them as they had come down in term time. The arguing at home still continued but while they were there they tried to keep it to mainly daunting each other and bickering. I would see my aunties looking at each other, obviously feeling uncomfortable at the tense atmosphere in the house. They would walk me to school everyday and collect me at the end of the day with Theresa. She was not used to being walked, so pulled, and with being a sleigh dog was hard to keep a hold of, but nevertheless to make me happy they would be stood with Theresa, waiting patiently at the school gate. I was sad to see them leave, and they never came back for a return visit.

A few weeks later as I was returning from school, my mum and Jerry were walking down our street with Theresa on her lead. Surprised, I rushed up to them asking where they were going. "We're taking her for dog training, so she walks better on her lead." Satisfied, I continued up to the house and let myself in. The house seemed empty with Theresa not being in to greet me as usual, but I understood she needed to be better on her lead. They seemed to be out for ages, and I wanted Theresa home, I wanted to cuddle her and tell her about my day so I found myself pacing waiting on their return. I heard the door open, and ran to the door to greet them, they both walked in and closed the back door after them. Confused, I reopened the door calling Theresa in, there was no sign of her, "Mum where's Thersa?" The panic was obvious in my voice. "She's gone, Danielle." Her words cut into me like a knife – gone, gone, how? Why? No, no it wasn't possible. I loved her she was my confidant, my best friend. How could they do this to me? I ran to my room in floods of tears. I hated her, I hated both of them, I would never ever forgive her for this, NEVER. I withdrew further into myself, not allowing anyone to get close so they could not hurt me – I was constantly thinking of my dog. Was she safe? Happy? Loved? Was she missing me as much as I missed her? The resentment for my mother was toxic, I was six years old, lonely, scared, had no one to turn to or trust. That's when the thumb-sucking began, I was always getting told off, but it was the only thing I found any comfort in.

The next school holiday there was no sitter, my mum would take me with her to the public house where she worked in the afternoon. I would take in books to read and colouring books, and the locals would involve me in their games of cards and dominoes and teach me how to play; they were kind to me and kept me amused while my mum worked to stop me getting bored and under her feet.

After work sometimes we would wander round the shops of Mansfield, we never bought anything, but it was nice to look and dream, and though I was still mad with my mum it was nice to spend a little time with her. One day on returning home we saw that Jerry was back from work early. He asked my mum general questions: What had she been up to? Who she had seen? etc. I sat on the sofa in total disbelieve as my mother made up this crazy elaborate story of how she had took me to the doctors, how the surgery was running late, and she wasn't sure if I was going to have to go back. I wanted to shout out "No, that's rubbish, why you saying these things? Stop lying," but I didn't dare. I knew it would cause trouble, plus if I spoke up I might lose out on spending time with my mum.

So I kept quiet, and listened intently as she was making up this elaborate untruth, puzzled at what her intentions were.

I was getting good at keeping secrets, keeping quiet; I never spoke up about my messed up family life. I don't know if it was because I was scared, felt a strange loyalty to my parents and didn't want them to get into trouble, or simply because there was no one to turn to or tell.

In an evening, I was left alone with Jerry looking after me, while my mum worked at the pub. On the whole he left me alone, finding me a burden and a nuisance to have to bother with. So he would send me up to bed early to get me out of his way. No matter what time it was I would never dare venture back down those stairs; I used to just lay there staring up at the ceiling till I drifted off to sleep.

On one of these evenings my mum had gone to work as normal, and about half an hour later a man turned up with a friend of his; they were both sat drinking beer and laughing and joking. I was sat on the floor, finishing off a jigsaw waiting for the inevitable, "Danielle, bed," I looked up at the clock it was way passed the usual time for me to be dismissed, but I wasn't going to say anything, I simply carried on playing, keeping quiet and hoping he might not notice me.

They were getting louder, laughing and joking as the beer cans piled up on the coffee table. "Danielle, come here." I got to my feet and went over waiting for, "OK Danielle, bed," but it never came. Still laughing he pulled my legs from under me so I fell backwards onto the carpet. In a flash he had pinned me down and was over the top of me, and I was screaming at the top of my voice: "Get off, leave me alone." He wasn't listening, he was laughing his head of, he held me steady and pinned me to the floor with one hand while using the other to tickle me. I had never been so scared and I was screaming, begging for him to stop. I hated every second of it, every second he had his hands on me. I was choking on the tears but he was relentless, laughing in my face, laughing at me squirming and wriggling on the floor trying to get away from his tormenting hands. When he let go I crawled sobbing into a corner of the sitting room at the side of the chair, trying to make myself so small, I would simply disappear. They were both pointing at me ridiculing me and laughing, this became a regular bedtime ritual when he had friends around. So I soon learned to put myself to bed as soon as one of his so-called mates showed up.

5

It was fast coming up to the six weeks holidays again, mum told me I would be staying with my grandparents again up North, that they would be having me every year in the main holiday, as she had to work. This time I was excited and pleased, it meant I would get to see them plus my aunties, and Tanya. I was still grieving over the loss of Theresa, and still bitter with my mum, so I was happy to be going.

We caught the coach as normal, again arriving in Newcastle late. When we got to my grandparents' they came rushing out to greet us, and once I entered their home I instantly felt safe. My mum had managed to persuade my grandma to allow Granddad to go out for a few drinks with her to the local pub. I could see my grandma wasn't happy about this, as my granddad wasn't a drinker, and according to her wasn't bothered about a pint. They went out laughing and joking like a couple of naughty teenagers let out for the night. I was in bed by the time they returned, and waking up the next morning, I was informed she had already left for her coach.

I started to blossom being at my grandparents'. I was allowed to laugh, play, mess about without any repercussions. My great aunts would collect Tanya and I everyday to go to the park, they seemed to know loads of people and would stand for what felt like ages chatting and catching up on the day. I didn't mind as I knew there was always that cornet on our return journey back to my gran's.

I was starting to understand their accent more, and enjoyed sitting and just listening to them chat, and trying to pick out weird and strange words I wasn't accustomed too. "Wey aye, man!", "Howay man!". It made me smile, especially when there was company round and everyone was speaking at once.

My grandparents didn't drive, but they decided we were going for a day at the seaside. The weather was glorious, so armed with all the essentials, packed lunch, sun cream, sun hat etc. – we all set off for Whitley Bay, even Tanya was allowed to come. It turned out to be a great day they bought me a bucket and spade, an ice cream, and we spent all day on the beach – me playing, and the adults with their trousers rolled up sunning on the beach. I ran poor Tanya off her tiny paws, running up and down the beach with her, playing and laughing. My granddad took some pictures to show my mum on her return, my mum had not been mentioned all holiday, and this cast a shadow on a perfect day knowing it would soon be over, and I would have to return back home. As my seventh birthday fell in the school holiday again, I celebrated it with my grandparents and aunts. My grandma had done everything perfectly just like the year before, and I never even noticed the absence of my parents.

My mum came to my grandparents' early, before the end of the six weeks holiday. They were surprised to see her. She told us she was back, as she needed to speak to me. Taking my hand, she led me to a chair and lifted me up onto her knee, a very unusual act to say the very least. Looking over at my grandparents, who were watching over curiously from the sidelines my mum began: "Danielle, I am afraid, I have some bad news for you." I twisted around on her lap so I could see her face as she spoke. "Danielle I am sorry to tell you that you won't be going back to your usual school."

Before I had a chance to respond my grandma jumped in, "What do you mean, she can't go back to her usual school? She is settled there, you can't just move her around willy nilly to suit your own selfish needs." My granddad took hold of my grandma's hand and slowly led her out of the room, her protesting all the way.

"Danielle, you will be moving school because the one you are at is closing. They are going to move the school to a new area and it's to far away, you would have to travel by bus, plus it's got a uniform policy, and to be honest I can't afford it. You will be going to your new school straight after this holiday." It had taken me ages to finally settle at my school I was slowly getting to know people, and was making new friends.

"Mum, will my new school be like my old one? Will everyone be walking round in funny outfits?"

She smiled at me and, trying to stop herself laughing, replied, "No, Danielle, they are habits, they're what nuns wear. Your old school was a Catholic school, the new one is, if you like, a normal school; everyone wears standard clothes." A Catholic school, nuns – none of it made any sense to me. "Danielle, try not to worry, it's a really nice school, and you will soon adapt and make new friends, local kids you can go out and play with." She lifted me off her knee and placed me on the floor. "Now, Danielle, you wait here, I need to explain all this to your gran."

Waiting in the lounge I could hear my grandma yelling at my mum, it sounded like it was getting pretty heated. I went to the big picture window and looked out onto the street, children were playing with a whip and spinning top, trying to see who could get it the furthest. I watched mesmerised thinking, *OK, so maybe it wouldn't be too bad changing schools, if I could find friends to play with like that.*

Finally, as no one had come to get me, and it appeared to have fallen quiet in the other room I went to join them. My grandma appeared to have calmed down, and my granddad was sat at the dining room table looking anxiously between the two of them. My mum had picked up a book and was sat reading, or pretending I'm not sure which, but the atmosphere was still tense. "Danielle, get your coat. We are going out for some air." It was my granddad speaking,

I retrieved my coat off the back of the diningroom chair and followed him outside.

My granddad held out his hand, and I took hold of it as he led me down the street. I had no idea where we were going; my granddad had never taken me out before on his own. He didn't speak, he simply led me down one street after another finally we arrived at the sea. There were big ships as huge as my little eyes could take in. "Wow Granddad, look at those." There must have been at least seven or eight of these ships tethered at the dockside

"I know, hinny, this is where I work. I help make these ships." I looked up at him, and realised I felt small at the side of him. *Wow, my granddad was a ship builder. Wow, how cool was that.* The ships laid out in front of us were all the colors under the rainbow. We carried on walking down the dock and he pointed out the cranes, explaining to me what they did and how they worked. We sat and watched the tide as my granddad rolled a cigarette. I was fascinated watching him roll his cigarettes, he usually did it in an evening, and I would sit and watch him for hours. He had a magic metal tin which opened up, he put the cigarette paper in a grove in the tin added his baccy, closed the tin and hey presto a cigarette popped out. On our return to the house my grandma and mum were chatting and everything appeared to be back to normal.

It was nice, having my mum staying with me at my grandparents'. She took me out to Newcastle for the day and pointed out some of the sights, and we had a return journey to the seaside. So when she told me it was time to pack up and go home I was gutted. Why couldn't we just stay here? It was nice here, there were people here that cared about me. I protested to my mum, "No Mum, I want to stay here a little longer," but all my protests fell on deaf ears.

"No, Danielle, we're going, and that's it. You'll be back next year and the year after that, plus you have a new school to start and new friends to make. It will be exciting. So now, Danielle, stop being silly, we're going."

We caught our usual coach back, I found it hard to settle, wondering what was waiting for me at home. My mum never stopped chatting on the way back, but I wasn't really listening, I was more focused on what was going to happen next. My mum held my hand walking up to the house, I didn't want to go in as I hated it there; I hated everything that went on behind those four walls.

6

Jerry, as I was to call him now, was not in, thankfully, so I was able to get unpacked and settled back in. I was watching television when he got back. He never even glanced at me, just sat in his usual seat, paper spread out in front of him. My mum was home in the days running up to me starting my new school, and we were out and about, busying ourselves with buying new clothes and shoes ready for me to start my new school as I had shot up over the summer holidays.

I was not worried about starting a new school, I trusted my mum and we had been getting along well since she came up North to collect me from my grandparents'.

The new school was bigger than my old one and again the building was sectioned of into two parts: the front being the primary school and the back junior school. There were two playgrounds either end; the younger children had their own, and so did the older children. The junior school playground was much bigger than mine, with large concrete tubes scattered around the yard, plenty big enough for children to sit in and hide, chat and shelter from the odd shower. The primary playground was made up of nothing but concrete with a hopscotch game marked out in white paint.

My teacher, Mrs Taylor, was lovely and helped me settle in her class immediately. The register was called as per usual in my old school, then we were taken to a large school hall for assembly, all the children in the school were gathered there, I nervously glanced around and I could not believe how many there were compared to my old school. The children were all shuffling on their feet, and chattering as a voice boomed out, "Silence in the hall, children, the headmistress is on her way." Instantly silence fell, there wasn't a whisper, in the middle of the hall was a podium raised off the floor with a resting table on top similar to what they use in church. A figure appeared, stood above us all. I looked up, and saw that it was a woman around fortyish, who was very conservatively dressed, and she spoke perfectly. All eyes were on her as she welcomed us back to the start of the term.

I stood staring at her, I couldn't believe what I was witnessing. She had split into two people, one above the other. I shook my head and looked again – yes, there were definitely two of her, as I was stood there closing my eyes, and reopening them. Tilting my head left and right, but no matter what there remained this second image of her floating in the air. Was I going mad? I looked around, no one else seemed to be witnessing anything unusual; they were all patiently waiting for her to finish and to be dismissed back to their classes. I knew no one in this school, no one I could confide this news too. As the day went on, I was busy finding my way around the new school, meeting new people, finding the dinner hall. So during the process of the day I forgot about the strange occurrence, until the next day and the next and so on when it happened every single time in assembly looking up at my headmistress on her platform.

My mum was taking me to and from school, while I settled in my first term. I loved her taking me and picking me up; we would chat about my day, and on the way to school we would call into the local fruit and veg shop where I was allowed to choose some fruit for my lunch. I had started to make a few friends who lived on my street, and after school I was allowed to play out with them for a while in the park at the top of our street.

I had settled in well in my first term, my mum was right, everyone was nice, and I was actually besotted by my new teacher Mrs Taylor. She didn't appear that old, maybe twenty or just over; she was slim with long black hair that flowed down her back, and she was so enthusiastic about her lessons that you couldn't help but get spurred along. She was always praising us, something I was not used to as praise was alien, so I revelled in it, wanting to do well in her class to make her proud of me.

I needed no encouragement to do any homework set, or do my reading and fill out my reading chart, as soon as I stepped indoors out would come any work set, and

I wouldn't look up till it was finished. My reading and spelling was improving and I worked hard to get top marks in any tests she set.

I was actually sad when it came to the end of my first term, again my mum had not organised a sitter, so I went into work with her each afternoon while she did her shift at the pub. The regulars welcomed me back with open arms again, allowing me to join in with their cards and dominoes by the end of the school holiday I had become quite a little hustler.

7

This term I was to take myself to school; there was a lollipop lady posted at both main roads so my mum said I would be fine. Hanging on to the sixpence in my hand for dear life I made the short journey to school. There were lots of young children being taken by their parents, some looking older than me, so I felt proud of myself as I skipped along merrily to school. I stopped only to look in the fruit and veg shop eagerly eyeing up what to spend my sixpence on. In the end I opted for an orange and stuffed it away inside my rucksack.

I went to class as usual, sat at my desk and patiently waited for my teacher, so excited to see her again. In she came as happy, optimistic, and smiley as ever. After doing the register we went to the hall as usual for assembly. As everyone stood there I looked at the platform, everything seemed OK. I raised my head higher as if someone was stood on it, and instantly saw double of the picture on the wall behind. What the hell was wrong with me? What was causing this strange phenomena? Looking nervously around no one seemed to be seeing this but me. I stood there praying for assembly to be over, for this torment to end, but no, everyday was the same. I hated those assemblies, hated that hall but mostly I hated that rotten platform.

In class, though, I was excelling, wanting to do nothing more than impress my favorite teacher. In tests I was top of my class, coming in either second or first every time, and I was lapping up every bit of attention she threw my way. We didn't always get homework, and on the days we didn't I would play either on the park, or by myself in the back garden.

My mum was cooking tea and she had told me not to wander off, so I was busy playing gardener in the back garden. Not that we had any plants, it was just grass and mainly dock leaves, but while I had been with my grandparents they had allowed me to help them tend their garden, and had got me my own small trowel and spade. So I was happily absorbed digging up dock leaves and carefully transplanting them into new parts of the garden. I was facing away from the kitchen door, but clearly heard my mum call me in for tea. Still on my hunches I turned to respond to her, and came face to face with a snake. The shock caused me to fall backwards onto my backside. it was raised up, and was the same height as me while sitting on my behind; its mouth was open and it was hissing like mad. Frantically trying to get away, I shuffled back on my bum, and as soon as there was enough distance between me and the snake I sprung to my feet, and ran screaming at the top my voice, "MUM, MUM!" Sweating and panting I raced into the kitchen.

"Danielle, stop your hollering, sit down and get your tea." Looking down at my plate, it was the meal from hell: brains faggots. The name was sickening without having to sample it. "But, Mum…"

"Danielle, I'm not telling you again, eat your food and you don't move from there till its gone." No way was I eating that, the smell was revolting. I picked up my fork and started pushing the food around on the plate, willing it somehow to evaporate. Who in their right mind eats brains? Not me for sure, I didn't care, I would sit here all night if I had to, I wasn't eating it, and that's that. I was still sitting there an hour later, refusing to touch the stuff, my mum finally realised this was one battle she wasn't winning. "OK, Danielle, go get ready for bed."

In the early hours of the morning, I woke up in a blind panic, my hair was sodden, and I was shaking like a leaf. The room was pitch black, I had this fear something was in the room with me. Too scared to move, I put the covers over my head. Closing my eyes tight, and pulling in the sheets as tight as I could, I attempted to go back to sleep.

I started to drift off to sleep, that's when the images started: I instantly opened my eyes, and the images went. I laid there, too scared to move or shout for help in case Jerry came in naked, which was more frightening than the images themselves, and I knew my mum was not home to comfort me. I was too scared though to close my eyes, as I would be tormented by the sickening sight. I kept fighting the sleep all night, but it soon got the better of me. The snakes were back – hissing and slithering they appeared huge in my nightmare. I was slowly being lowered head first into a deep hole full of snakes of all sizes and colours; I was screaming and wriggling like crazy as the snakes were getting closer and closer to me, but suddenly they were gone and I fell fast asleep. This became a reoccurring dream, haunting me for months as soon as I got into bed, and closed my eyes. They were back frightening me every single night, and I was a terrified little girl, to scared too ask for help.

I was going into school, tired everyday. I was struggling with the work and as I was unable to fully concentrate, and I even fell asleep in class once. Mrs Taylor sent me to the sick bay, where I laid on a long couch and slept until home time. I was sent home with a note for my mum, and the following day she kept me off school. Her and Jerry were both working, so I was left on my own, as they had no time to arrange child care and my mum was doing a stock check in the pub.

When I woke that morning the house was empty, I went slowly downstairs, my mum had left a bowl of cereal out for me and a glass of milk. It was cold in the house as it was winter and there were no fires lit, but in the sitting room they had left one bar on the calor gas heater, I settled down in front of it dithering, and tucked into my breakfast. The heat from the calor gas heater was warming and comforting, but you had to sit virtually on top of it, to feel the benefit of it, so the rest of the house was like an ice box.

After breakfast I decided, as I would probably be on my own a long time and it was still early, I would play with my

42

toys in front of the heater. I ran upstairs collected three of my dolls, a large brown teddy bear, and a small china tea set that I had been given for my birthday. Placing the toys in front of the heater in a circle, with the teaset, set out in the middle, I set up a teddy bears' picnic, I had no food, so I was pretending to feed each toy sandwiches, cake, tea etc;.

The most important toy was not cooperating though, and kept over balancing, I thought about putting him to one side, but you can't have a teddy bears' picnic without the bear, so I persevered. No matter how many times I sat him up, he toppled over. Getting sick of it, as he was ruining my game, I lent him up against the calor gas heater. Finally he stayed put.

I was totally absorbed in my game, everyone was getting their fair share of food, and we had moved on to play ring a ring of roses, when suddenly there was a strange haze rising from the bear, and a funny smell; pulling the bear from the heater, the smell got worse. I turned him over and his back was all singed and blackened – *oh no*! What was I going to do? I ran, still holding the bear, to the back door. The smell was travelling through the house, following my every turn. I reached for the handle and pulled on it but it didn't budge it was locked. No, no, no, what was I going to do? I frantically ran back into the sitting room and tried the front door, that was locked too. Tears were welling up in my eyes, as I was panicking. I was really for it now. Looking around the room, the only thing I could think of was to hide it, the bear was still smoldering as I threw it behind the sofa that was up against the main wall.

8

My mum and Jerry both arrived home together a few hours later, the smell, though still there, was not quite so toxic. As they walked in they were laughing and joking, I looked over nervously to the sofa expecting my crime to be discovered there and then.

But no, they just went through into the kitchen, Jerry chatting away to my mum, while she busied herself rustling up some food. In fact nothing was said all day, and when I went up to bed I wasn't sure if I was relieved or not. I laid awake, waiting for my bedroom door to fly open, and for Jerry to drag me out of bed in a fit of temper and possibly drowning me down the toilet this time.

Maybe, I should have confessed – what if the house burnt down while we slept? *Oh no what had I done?* I laid awake for ages, with thoughts going round and round in my head. I wanted to get up, go running into my mum's bedroom and tell her the whole story, but he was there, and

I didn't know what he would do if I did. So I kept quiet, and eventually fell asleep; there were no snakes that night.

I was awake early the following morning, waiting for the consequences. Finally my mum came in. "Come on, sleepy head, it's time for school." I slowly got up, and got dressed for school, steeling myself as I went downstairs. I didn't get it, surely they must have found the bear due to the smell. Was this some kind of sick trick, and they were going to pounce on me when I walked in.

Jerry had gone to work, so with a deep breath I anxiously entered the kitchen where my mum was. "Morning Danielle, sit yourself down. I will sort your breakfast." I did as instructed immediately, intently watching my mum as she busied herself. The morning carried on normally, both of us doing our usual routine. As I left the house for my usual walk to school I took a deep breath; I don't know how but I'd got away with it, I survived.

All the while at school, my mind was on what had happened, and how I got away with it. I could not believe it. On my return from school, nothing was said, and as the weeks passed I forgot about my abandoned friend behind the sofa, and life just carried on as normal.

The snakes were still haunting me every single night; I just wanted them to go away and leave me alone. I was still finding it hard to concentrate at school, but I was determined to make Mrs Taylor proud so I persevered with my studies regardless of the fatigue

On my return from school, the only source of heat

again was the calor gas heater, so I settled myself down in front of it and got stuck into my latest school project. While deep in concentration my mum came in to the room. "Danielle, what on earth were you thinking of?" I didn't look up, I was busy trying to construct a space rocket out of old bottles and bits of rags and foil. "Christ, Danielle, you could have burnt the house down." My heart sunk, and I nervously looked up from where I was sat on the floor.Oh no! My crime had been discovered. I looked nervously around, trying to gather my thoughts and work out where Jerry was. Looking at her, though, she didn't appear cross, more concerned. "Danielle, come sit on the sofa with me, there is something I need to tell you.

"Danielle, when you were two, maybe two and a half, we lived in a bed sit on Woodhouse Road. The house had a front garden that led out onto a main busy road. You were playing on the front garden, and when I went to call you in, you had gone. You had managed to open the latch on the gate, cross three main roads, how you did it and survived I will never know. Eventually a bus driver going on shift picked you up and took you to the bus station depot. When I finally found you, there you were happy as Larry in the bus station canteen, the table you were sat at covered in sweet wrappers, crisps and spilt bottles of pop. You were being well and truly spoilt, in fact you screamed the place down when we left.

"What I am trying to get across, Danielle, is that you need to be careful. You can not do things that aren't safe; eventually your luck will run out. It's me that's left having to explain what happened, and face the consequences of

46

your actions." I looked at her blankly, I had been two, how could I be responsible for my own actions? Surely it was her job to keep me safe – if she had been watching me like any right-minded parent would have, I'd not have been in that position, being stuffed full of goodies by well-meaning bus drivers. I found the story fascinating though, and prompted her to tell me more.

She explained that when my dad died, the house we lived in was taken back by the pit authority. We were not allowed to stay there as it was a house tied in with the job, so we had moved around a lot, eventually settling into the bedsit on Woodhouse Road. She said it had been hard when he died, money had been tight, and that we had struggled until she married Jerry, and bought the house we are in now. She explained that my grandparents from up North had given them the down payment on the house. I loved listening to her as it was very rare she talked to me in this way, so to hear her speak about my dad, and my past was fascinating. I was finally letting go of the past, how she got rid of Theresa, and letting her in, feeling like I had my mum, but if only for a short time.

9

The incident with the bear was never mentioned again, and I am not sure if she told Jerry about it or not. He never spoke of it, so maybe she was more aware of the goings on in the house than she was letting on, and feared the rage of his anger and the consequences of his actions if she had told him.

The six weeks school holiday soon came around, and I happily boarded the coach with my mum. As usual we were greeted by my grandparents, who were happy to see us both. I loved it there, I loved coming each year, and now I didn't care when my mum left first thing the next day – I happily waved her off. Tanya the corgi was still there every year to greet me, as was the white teddy bear positioned as always on the pillow with his arms stretched out. It was a welcoming sight, it was a comforting sight; it was good to know some things were steadfast, and it made me feel safe and secure being there.

My great aunts came like clockwork to take Tanya and I for our daily walk. I was learning more about them as they were opening up about themselves. They told me they were my grandma's sisters, and they had never married so had always lived together. In their working life they had run a local green grocer's shop.When they finally retired, they sold the business and bought a flat, in addition to the one they already owned, and rented it out to one of my uncles."

It was hard to believe they were sisters, they were so different in character: my aunty Beth was quiet, shy and withdrawn, while aunty Ettie never stopped talking and instigated every conversation with the locals on our daily walks, she was always bubbly, laughing and smiling and a joy to be with.

Neither of them ever said a cross word to me, and I was always on my best behaviour, after all I was not jeopardising getting my cornet on the way home. The weather as always was glorious, so they had arranged with my grandparents, to take Tanya and I to the Forest of Dean for a day out. We caught the bus and arrived at this wonderful country park, full of babbling brooks, waterfalls and rope bridges. I loved it, running around with Tanya, climbing and exploring, by the time the day was over we had walked our legs off. On our return my grandma had laid on a full spread, and my aunties stayed and tucked into it. We had all had a fabulous day.

On my birthday that year, I was not as excited. My grandma had laid on her traditional birthday tea, baked, and put in all the effort, but this time I wanted my mum. I felt we were getting on better and though I was happy with my family up North and I was well cared for, it would have been nice if, just for once, she was there for my birthday. I had received a kite this year off my grandparents and my granddad was excitedly wanting the party to be over, so he could take me on to the school field that backed onto the house to fly it.

On the field my granddad carefully unwrapped the kite and unravelled the string. It was bright blue and yellow with pictures of ships on either side. "Right, hinny, you hold the string as tight as you can, and run as fast as you can, and as you run the kite will soar up into the sky." So, doing as instructed, I took hold of the string on the kite, and ran as fast as my little legs would allow. I looked back to see if the kite was up, but no it was just dragging along the ground. "Danielle, look where you're going." The words had scarcely left his mouth when I went spilling over onto the grass as the string tangled around my feet. My granddad came running up, laughing. "Up you get, hinny." Taking my hand, and with us both taking a firm hold of the string, we began to run. "That's it. Run, run, run, fast as your feet will carry you," he was gasping in my ear. "Right, stop, Danielle." Spinning round I saw the kite soaring through the air. We both flew that kite until it became dark and we were unable to see it in the sky anymore. Carefully packing the kite away we returned back home, both of us laughing and joking about our adventure.

The days were flying by, and soon my mum was back to collect me; she had come down a few days early to spend time catching up with the relatives. On her first night she persuaded grandma to let granddad out for a few hours to the local public house. My mum thought it was a great thing getting one over on my grandma, who tended to rule the roost at home, and granddad according to my mum was not allowed anywhere without her blessing. I was still up when they got back. As I was eight years old and as it was the holiday I was allowed to stay up until ten, which meant I got supper with the grown ups that consisted of a slice of toast and jam and a couple of biscuits, usually custard creams.

The next day my mum took me to a local hairdressers to get my hair cut, ready for the new term. On our return my grandma and mum ended up having heated words about me. "Laura, I sometimes wonder if you give a high hooter about that kid. Look at her!"

My mum stared over at me, "She looks fine to me, what am I supposed to be looking at? In fact I think they have done a smashing job of her hair." My gran was now livid.

"Laura, if that kid's not wearing spectacles by the time she gets back here next year, I swear on my life, I will take her and sort her out myself. How on earth she can see anything is beyond me, the poor mite."

My mum looked over at me, puzzled, obviously not knowing the foggiest what she meant, "Well she looks OK to me."

That was it, my gran was on the ceiling. "Laura, do you ever actually look at her, take any notice of her, in fact, or

are you just to wrapped up in yourself, you selfish mare."
This had visibly shaken my mum being chastised by my
gran, so she promised as soon as we got back she would
take me to a local opticians. My gran seemed satisfied with
this simply repeating, "Mark my words if you don't there
will be consequences."

10

I started the new term with a bright red, new pair of NHS spectacles. I wasn't keen on wearing them, as they pinched my nose and made it red and sore. The optician had been nice and explained everything to me on a level I could understand; he explained to me that my left eye was weaker than my right, so my right eye had to work harder to compensate. He said that if the glasses didn't work to straighten out my vision, I would need an operation at some point in the future. He also referred us to King's Mill, our local hospital, so I could have regular check ups on my eyes, these were going to be every three months getting less over time if there was a dramatic improvement.

The start of a new academic term meant my class was in another classroom further along the corridor, we all sat there nervously waiting on the arrival of our new teacher. I was secretly praying Mrs Taylor would walk in, but no this year a male teacher walked in. Without saying a word, he picked up the chalk and wrote in big letters "Mr Wilcox"; instantly I knew I wasn't going to like him.

He was an old-fashioned teacher who ruled with a rod of iron, who expected silence in the class, everyone to sit up straight in their chairs and only speak when spoken too. He walked around the classroom slapping a ruler into the palm of his hand chanting times tables and lyrics that we had to chant along to, there was never any trouble in his class no one would dare speak out of turn.

Assemblies were always the same; we were led into the big hall, and the headmistress gave the assembly from her platform. Looking up at her I still had the double vision the glasses had not cured this, hopefully this would get sorted in time. I would look up at the raised second image of the headmistress floating in the air, and I had discovered if I moved my head slightly in different directions I could get the image to move in different directions, even making her raise higher or lower depending how I tilted my head. I was no longer scared of this strange phenomenon it had become a normal part of my life, a normal part of who I was.

Of course I got the usual teasing – specky, four eyes etc – but it never really bothered me, after all it was normally the children from deprived homes or others with their own image issues. Of course it hurt my feelings, I was a sensitive eight-year-old with my own issues, but I would never let them know they were getting to me. Some of the children in my class took a disliking to me because I always got top marks, while they seemed to be struggling at their lessons.

One girl in particular took against me, her name was Dawn Clarke and she was in my class. She also lived at the bottom of my street, she came from a family of ten with five brothers and three sisters, I had never done anything to her, never even really spoke two words to her, but for some reason she hated the very sight of me, and she wasn't afraid to let me know. As I was only slim I always did well in physical education; I could run laps around the school field and not really get out of breath and I got every single swimming badge going and loved it. I could twist and turn myself into every position in stretch class and never fell off the balance beams. Dawn was the same age as me but she was a big girl, and easily three times my weight. She would try to run and end up gagging for breath; she was embarrassed at having to wear her overtight pinching swimsuit, and any twisting and turning she tried would end up with her falling flat on her face with the other children pointing and glaring at her. No one would actually dare laugh at her, however, as she was the class bully, and no one wanted her on their case.

I was the smallest in the class, maybe that is why she started – probably figured I was an easy target. I had no brothers or sisters to stick up for me. So every chance she got she would set on me, it started as basic name calling which I ignored, then the odd jab passing her in the school corridors.

Then one evening after school, I had stayed behind with some other children who had been chosen for the school play, it was *Alice in Wonderland*, and I was the Cheshire cat in the play. I only had a line but still everyone had to stay behind once a week for the rehearsals. It was dark when I left school; a lot of the parents had picked their children up, so as I walked through the playground to the main gate the place was deserted.

Suddenly out of nowhere there was Dawn, and around her were another four children I didn't recognise, I looked around trying to figure out my escape but there was nowhere to go. Slowly they walked up to me, and led me into one of the school shelters the four younger children started to yell, shouting at her to punch me and egging her on, she raised her fist and punched me in the side of the ribs, the kids were spurring her on with their endless chanting. More blows rained down on me as I covered my head to try to protect myself. Finally she seemed to get bored with the whole situation, pulled me by the arm out of the circle of children, and told me to flee for my life.

It was a good fifteen minutes back to my house, but I ran all the way, choking on tears and never once looking back. When I got back the house was empty, so I let myself in with the key mum left under the bin. There was a dinner on the side for me, which I struggled to eat. It was late when Jerry got back; he was accompanied by one of his friends and, as I could not cope with anymore grief, I retired up to my room, got into bed only to be tormented by the dreaded snakes. When was this ever going to end?

The following week at our usual after-school rehearsal, I could not concentrate, I was conscious of the fact that when this was over I had to walk back home alone. I was constantly being reprimanded by the teacher in charge, who was taking it all very seriously, wanting it all to be perfect for the watching crowd on the opening night. "Danielle, if I have to tell you one more time to stop talking I'll seriously flip." We were eight years old, it was not going to be a Shakespearean play it was meant to be a bit of fun and I felt like telling her to get a grip. In the end she gave up, glaring over at me. "That's it, I have had enough. We will call it a night." The other children sat chatting, waiting for their lifts or parents to pick them up, but I knew I had to face going outside in the dark, crossing the empty, spooky playground.

As I opened the door leading to the playground, I peeked out, cautiously eyeing up the area. It looked a long way to the school gate that led to the street; it was pitch black, the couple of lights on in the playground made it look intimidating and scary. I looked behind me to see if anyone else was following me but no one was there, all I could hear was the children laughing and chatting in the school hall. I couldn't hide here all night. I could hear my heart pounding as I ran at full-pelt across the playground, I made it to the school gate. Hurling it open, I ran like I had the Devil himself chasing me. Every street corner I turned, I expected to run into them but as we had left early maybe they were on their way up to the school to get me. I went an alternative route, not knowing if it was their usual route or not, I just knew I was not passing their front door. Finally, I made it back in one piece; as usual the house was in darkness. I retrieved the key and let myself in, locking it right behind me. Putting the light on I caught a glimpse of myself in the mirror, my face was flushed, my cheeks were burning, I fell into a nearby chair, panting and struggling to get my breath.

11

On my way to school the following week a girl came running up to me, talking away at ten miles an hour. "Hi I'm Debra, I have just moved onto the street. I live six doors down from you, can I walk with you to school?" Debra was smaller than me, with dark short hair and a willing smile. "My mum says I need to make new friends, will you be my friend? I am seven, by the way, how old are you?" She never waited for a response just carried on rattling on about herself and her family all the way to school. As we arrived at the school gates she ran ahead, skipping up to the line of waiting children. "See you later, I'll look out for you," she yelled at the top of her voice, as she took her place at the back of the queue.

As I left school at the end of the day, she had attached herself onto Dawn's younger sister Anne, as they were in the same class. I could see Dawn glaring at this outsider, and it was obvious she was not happy with Debra tagging along with them. Debra appeared oblivious to Dawn, and was laughing and joking with her new friend.

Anne and Debra soon became best friends, a situation her elder sister detested and every chance she got she would beat poor Debra up, who would then go crying back to her mum. Debra's mum would be forever out on the street screaming and shouting at us kids. "I am sick to death of you lot picking on my Debra, if I have to come out one more time, I won't be responsible for my actions." Dawn and her hangers on just stood in the middle of the street jeering at her and laughing, I had been sent to the shop by my mum to get some milk and was stood intently listening to their outbursts.

Finally Debra's mum, exasperated and embarrassed, went back indoors, and I went ahead to get the milk as instructed. On my return from the shop she was out again swearing, ranting and raving at Dawn and her friends; you could see she was absolutely livid. I walked up the street but could not pass Dawn and her friends as they were blocking my route, so I stood at the back of everyone waiting for space to pass. Dawn jeered at her and swore back. That was it, Debra's mum tore down the street looking like she would murder the first person she got hold of; the crowd blocking my route turned on their heels sending me flying and the milk smashing to the ground. They ran by me, and I could see Debra's mum tearing towards me so I also ran down the street after the others. They all ran down the passage that led to Dawn's back door with me lagging well behind. As I turned the corner that led to her back door I heard the door slam as they all disappeared inside, and

I was trapped in her yard totally on my own with Debra's mum bearing down on me. There was no where to go and I was trapped so I curled myself up in the fetal position and waited for the onslaught. I glanced up, she was panting as she grabbed me by my arm and dragged me to my feet. "Right, you little bitch, you are coming with me, let's see what your mother has to say about this."

All the way up the street to mine, she was pulling, pushing and pinching me. With me in tears, we arrived at my back door. She was hammering down the back door, when my mum answered. With my mum standing there looking totally perplexed Debra's mum started on her rant, telling her I was a bitch, I was constantly bullying her daughter, and if it didn't stop she was involving the police, she said it was about time she sorted me out. My mum simply looked passed her and said, "Danielle where's my milk."

Stuttering I responded, "I had dropped it." Debra's mum's mouth dropped open as my mum went onto explain that I had been indoors all day and only gone out to run an errand. She said not to darken her door again with allegations that had no validation to them, and that it would be her calling the police if she continued threatening a minor. Now it was Debra's mums turn to stutter. Looking completely shocked and gobsmacked she made her apologises and left.

When I got in she asked me what happened I told her the whole story. She was livid and went round to see her, on her return she simply said, "Don't worry, hun, she won't dare ever bother you again." I was so proud of my mum, she had actually stuck up for me for the first time ever, wow she was my hero. I had come to realise that my mum was the only person I really had in my life, the rest of my family lived to far away, she was far from perfect, but she was consistent, reliable and now I knew she loved me in her own way.

12

As usual I went to stay with my grandparents up north for the summer holidays, when we arrived there were other people also there. It turned out it was my auntie and uncle from Middlesex, and they had come up with their son Darren. I didn't care less who they were, all I knew was this boy much younger than me was stood holding my bear, the bear that greeted me every year like clockwork. How dare they, how dare he stand there blatantly holding MY bear. I went over and snatched it back. "Danielle, give it him back this instant. Darren was here first so he gets the bear." I glared up at my gran, hating her. It was mine, it had always been mine, how dare they. I ran up to my room and sobbed into the pillow and refused to go back down till tea time.

He was still clutching my bear when I went back downstairs, the adults were sat chatting, my auntie was saying she would stay a few days until she knew Darren was settled, and then leave him, and pick him up in a couple of weeks. Oh no I was going to be stuck with him for a couple of weeks. The following day my mum left as usual, but Darren's parents stayed as promised. I would watch them playing with him laughing and joking. He would be running around giggling his head off while his parents were playing kiss-chase with him etc; there was no doubting they idolised him.

On their last evening before leaving Darren, they were scanning through the papers, chatting with Darren asking him what he would like to see at the pictures that evening. His mum turned to me and asked if I knew of any decent films to go and see. Looking at her blankly I shook my head not knowing what she meant. "Danielle, have you never been to the pictures to watch a film?" Again I shook my head, appearing shocked, she returned her attention back to her son. "*Bambi*'s on, Darren, that has good reviews we will go see that." I watched them that evening ready to go out all smartly dressed. Darren was excited as he had been promised virtually every treat in the cinema. As they left I felt a tinge of jealousy, why had I not been to the cinema? And what was all the fuss about? I felt like I was missing out.

Why wasn't my mum like that with me? I couldn't remember the last time we had laughed together or my mum had shown me any real attention. The only time we went out was on an odd evening when I would be sat on my own with a packet of crisps and a bottle of pop – if she remembered to come back with them, that is. I was

64

left there until closing time or whenever she got fed up, as I was not allowed in the main bar. Every once in awhile though she would pop back to check if I was OK and bring me some refreshments. It was boring sitting there all night; there was a clock on the wall that never seemed to move, and there was nothing in the room but a few shabby tables and chairs.

When they returned from the cinema, they were raving about how good it was, and how his mum had cried when the deer was shot. Darren was loaded up with goodies: pick and mix, popcorn, candy floss a large pop – way more than any small child could eat. He was giving it a good try though, stuffing handful after handful into his mouth, until his cheeks were bursting. I had never seen anything like it in my life. Eventually his mum told him to leave them until the next day as he would make himself sick. Under protest he handed them over to his mum. He spent the rest of the evening tearing around like a maniac, his mum said, "It was probably too many e-numbers."

The following morning they said their goodbyes, reassuring Darren they would be back before he knew it, There were a few tears off Darren as they left, but once given back his cinema treats he soon cheered up. My aunties turned up as usual for Tanya's walk, this time Darren also came with us. It was an awkward couple of hours with neither of us knowing what to say to each other. On our return Darren went hunting out granddad and I played with Tanya; for the rest of the holiday we tolerated each other. One evening the telephone rang. "Darren, it's your mum, she as rang to check up on you."

Taking the telephone he was excitedly chatting away to his parents, who were on the other end listening, to his holiday adventures. There it was again eating at me, I didn't even know my grandparents owned a phone, I had never ever seen them use it, and it had never rang while I had been there, but here it was ringing for him, his concerned parents checking he was well. Didn't my mum ever wonder or worry if I was OK? Or was she just pleased to be shot of me for the six weeks – out of sight out of mind.

Darren's parents arrived the following week; they stayed a few days before returning back to Middlesex with Darren. I was pleased to see him go but funnily enough when he left, the house seemed empty. I had gone and retrieved my bear from his room and settled him back in my bed, but it was not the same, as he now felt tarnished and used, so after a couple of days I tossed him out of bed to be neglected for the rest of the holiday on my bedroom floor. It was nice to have my aunts and grandparents back to myself for the remainder of the holiday. My mum showed up as usual, and had not even taken her coat off, before persuading my grandma to let my granddad out for a few hours to go to the pub with her. When they returned I was already in bed, and the next day we said our goodbyes and left on the coach back to Mansfield.

13

In the summer holiday I had turned nine years old, and had shot up in the six weeks break. I was of average height for my age but I was lanky with hazel eyes and brown hair. My mum had allowed me to start growing my hair as it had always been kept short before; it had grown into my neck and I'd had it cut into a smart bob ready for the new term. My mum and I had gone into Mansfield and brought me a brand new wardrobe of clothes, as I had grown out of every item I owned, after we had lunch in town that was a special treat as we never ate out.

I had been to the hospital for my usual check up and they were pleased with the progress, so they were holding off with any eye operations and going to give the spectacles a chance to do there job first. I still had the double vision, but my left eye had started to straighten out a little, though it was still noticeable and I was told I would probably have to wear glasses indefinitely. They had prescribed a new prescription though, and I chose purple frames this time; they were identical to my old ones being free of the NHS just simply a different colour.

I was dreading going back to school. I knew I had to pass Dawn's house on the way to school or do the detour as I had on that fateful night of the school rehearsal, either way I knew she would get me, unless she had found some other poor victim. I decided to go the long way on my first day to avoid bumping into her and her mates; I did this for weeks and fortunately there was no sign of her, so I thought, *Right, Danielle, stop being a total wimp*, and as it was raining it made my mind up to walk the normal way home.

As I turned onto my street, there she was on her own stood outside her house. I looked around to see if there were any adults walking up or down the street but there was no one around. I crossed the road to avoid her, glancing across I could see her looking at me with total hatred in her eyes, "Danielle, you little shit, get here." I was going no where near her, and ran up the street with her chasing after me. "You wait till I get my fucking hands on you. I fucking hate you." She had picked up half a house brick, and to say she was so fat she had nearly caught me up. I tore round the corner of my house into the passage. "I'm going to fucking kill you." She raised the brick and launched it up the passageway with such force it hit the wall opposite to where I was running and rebounded on to the other wall, missing me by inches and shattering as it landed on the ground. She gave out a great big sigh, and yelled up the passage, "I'll get you next time, bitch."

I ran up to the back door and pulled down the handle like my life depended on it, but it didn't budge, thankfully Dawn had retreated, probably thinking my parents would have been in so had not dared follow me. I got the key from the usual hiding place and let myself in. I was shaking like a leaf. Christ she could have killed me, what was her problem? Why did she hate me enough to want to cave my skull in with a house brick? I sat in the dark until Jerry got in, too scared to make a sound, or even put a light on in case she came back, and maybe this time bringing her so-called mates. I kept imagining myself face down in the passage, blood pouring out the back of my head, alive, but suffering, maybe even slowly bleeding to death, no one knowing I was there; Jerry eventually finding me pale and cold laid out on the passage floor, with half a brick shattered at the side of me and Dawn not giving a damn about her actions and simply leaving me to rot.

As usual I never said anything, I had got to the point where there was no point, no one was there, and no one was listening anyway, plus if I did say anything would it make things worse for me. I never walked by Dawn's door again no matter what. I walked the long way home and it worked for me, I never really saw her, and if she was outside her house, it was too far and too steep a street, for her to attempt to catch me. I would be well gone by the time she got to the top.

I was enjoying this term in school my teacher was nice and the children were the same ones I had gone through the other years with. The school holiday was spent with my mum at her work playing cards and dominoes with the locals so all in all I was pretty settled, even Jerry had backed off some. So the only demons I had were Dawn and my continuous nightmares although even though these were frightening I had come to accept them as normal. I would go to bed knowing it would be the first thing I would see as I drifted off to sleep; the snakes of all sizes and various colours, with venomous, hissing, wanting to sink their fangs into me. I would seem to get to the point of sheer panic in these nightmares and then simply drift off – it was bizzare.

14

I don't know if it was my mum or Jerry, but we now owned a brand new colour television, not many people had one of these, and we were all excited when it was switched on for the first time. Wow, the colours simply exploded all over the screen as it was switched on, none of us could pull our eyes away from it, it was simply hypnotising.

I was engrossed in the television, watching some wildlife programme on a Sunday afternoon. My mum walked over to me from the kitchen where she had been preparing Sunday lunch. "Danielle, your dad's here." Not even looking away from the television I simply replied "No he's not, he's dead." Sighing my mum took my hand "Danielle, come with me." Leading me to the back door, I peered from behind her, standing in the doorway was a man, a stranger, dressed in a light grey suit, black shiny shoes, of medium height and build with black short hair that was combed back off his face.

I glanced up at my mum, confused to say the very least. "Danielle this is your dad, and he is going to take you out for the day." My mouth dropped agape, and before I could reason out this madness and protest she had bundled me out of the door and closed it behind me. So there I was stood with this man, what the hell was I supposed to make of this. He was the first to speak: "My car's parked round the front, Danielle, I thought we could go for a drive and then get some dinner." I followed him, hesitantly down the passage and onto the street. Parked at the front of our house was a huge silver shiny car; I had no idea what it was, but I could tell it was expensive. He unlocked the back door and opened it, holding on to the car door while I hauled myself in and sat on the back seat, the smell of leather hit you as soon as you got in the car it was immaculate and spotless.

We sat in silence, as he drove, I was in total shock, unable to speak or take any of these new events in. My dad was dead, yet here he was, I was sat in his car and he was driving. How was any of this even possible? Why had my mum lied all these years? Where had he been? Why had I not seen him until now? Questions were spinning round and round in my head, but I was to shell shocked to speak, to utter a single syllable, I was nine years old, how could this be happening? I had come to terms with the fact he was dead, I never knew him, so I couldn't really grieve for him, but now this.

He pulled up outside a nice semi-detached property, holding open the car door for me I climbed out. "This is where I live, Danielle, I just need to pop in for a few minutes, and then we will go get some dinner." He had the same accent as my mum, a northern accent, but not as broad as my grandparents'. I followed him in through the front door into his house, the place like his car was immaculate, entering the front room there was a woman there, slim, taller than my mum with black shoulder-length hair. "Danielle this is Maureen," I never said a word, I was looking at the huge bowl of fruit on their dining room table; I had never seen anything like it. He exchanged a few words with the woman, then beckoned me to sit with him on the sofa, where a photo album was laying, he proceeded to turn the pages telling me who this relation was and that relation was, it was all a blur to me and meaningless. This was all wrong, I had not been prepared for any of this, I just wanted to go home, it wasn't perfect back home but at least there I knew where I fitted in.

Finally he put down the photo album, said his farewells to Maureen, who had not spoken a single word to me, she simply appeared awkward and uncomfortable, not even sitting down just pacing the room the entire visit. We got back in the car, and arrived at a really fancy restaurant the sign said The Halfway Inn. I had never been here before or anywhere like it, but knew I was going to feel awkward and out of place. On entering you were greeted by the sound of families dining, children laughing and the hustle and bustle of a very busy place with waiters rushing here, there and everywhere. We stood at a sign that said wait here for service, we were soon escorted to a table for two, my dad handed me a menu and I looked at it awkwardly,

I had never been given a menu, mind know how to chose from one. "I think I will have the Sunday dinner," my dad announced. "Have you decided, Danielle?" Panic hit me I had no idea what to choose. Looking at the menu again I chose the first thing I saw, luckily it turned out to be burger and chips.

"Danielle, it's lovely to meet you, I think about you all the time." I glanced up at him, how the hell was I meant to answer that?

"OK, yes, Dad, nice to see you're alive and well," somehow didn't seem apropriate so I simply pushed the food around on my plate trying to avoid eye contact. This was so awkward and uncomfortable I wanted the ground to swallow me up. Finally I made an excuse saying I needed the toilet. I was shaking when I entered the toilet, I literally wanted to hide in there until my mum came and picked me up. I decided though I did actually need the toilet. When I had finished I went to slide the lock across but it wouldn't budge. I tried several times. Oh no I was locked in! I was just about to bang on the door for help when a woman's voice rang out, "You OK in there? Your dad sent me to check on you." I explained I was locked in and she released the latch from her side. Thanking her and relieved I went back to our table. "You OK? I was worried, that's why I sent the lady in to check on you." I explained what had happened and my dad laughed, "That's OK then, I thought you had ran out on me."

After dinner my dad took me shopping. It was October and my mum in her haste to bundle me out the house had

74

not even thrown a coat out after me. "My word, Danielle, there's not an ounce of fat on you to keep you warm. Where is your coat? You must be frozen." He led me into what appeared to be a really fancy clothes shop, marched over to the children's section and handed me a long, cream, fur coat. "Do you like this?" What nine year old wouldn't? He held it open while I put my arms through the sleeves. Wow it was so plush and soft I had never ever had anything like this ever. "There's a mirror over here, Danielle, come give us a twirl." I ran over to the mirror excited to see myself in hopefully my new coat. Oh my it was fab, I loved it, I twirled around as instructed, my dad laughing at me. "So do you like it?" Suddenly I had found my voice.

"Yes, yes, yes, I love it, can I really have it?"

"I insist. I can't have my only daughter freezing to death now, can I?" I refused to take it off so the assistant removed the tags so I could keep it on and show it off to my mum when I got home.

After, my dad dropped me off on the front street. "See you next week, Danielle." Beaming I waved him off. I ran into the house and my mum instantly stood up when I entered. "Mum, look, look, I got a new coat, aint it lovely?" My mum stood there, her mouth agape not knowing what to say, taking it off I handed it to her. "Mum put it somewhere safe until next week." Folding the coat up she replied, "Next week, why what's happening next week?"

"My dad says he is taking me out again."

15

The following Sunday, wearing the new coat my dad had bought me and the new dress, stockings and pumps my mum had got me that week, I waited patiently for my dad's return. I felt like a princess as I had never had clothes as nice before. I had still not processed this new turn of events, except I knew my mum had lied and my dad was alive and well. Why would you lie about something as horrific as that? It made no sense. I needed to ask her about it, as it was niggling away at me, eating away at me. I needed answers. So I had decided once this visit was over I would ask her, ask her when she seemed plyable and wouldn't jump down my throat. After all she must be expecting me to ask at some point surely.

I was waiting on the front street where my mum had sent me to wait, I was still not sure about any of this, but I was too young to put into words how I felt, to get it over to anyone how mixed up I felt. This person even though he is saying he is my dad feels nothing but a stranger to me. Anyone could have turned up and said, "Hi Danielle, I'm your dad, let's go play." Even though my mum had said all this time he was dead, and died in a car crash I had never seen a single picture of my real dad. There were no pictures up in the house of him, none of any of us in fact, that may have been why I never thought of it till now. My dad's house had photographs of him and Maureen up, photo albums of his and supposedly my relations – not that I knew any of them they were all just strangers to me. Yet I had never seen one solitary picture at mine, I had never even thought about it until now; this had most likely been brought on by the pictures I was shown last week.

I was not waiting long when his car drew up, he jumped out beaming and opened the back car door for me while I jumped in. "Hello, beautiful, how has school been?" I found it easier to speak to him this week and the conversation was simple, just general questions such as "What do you want to be when you grow up?" and "How is the family up north?" It seemed funny listening to him talk about my grandparents and relatives up north, it made it all seem more real, he obviously knew these people as he was going into depth talking away about them.

I had no idea where we were going, he never said. "Danielle, have you ever been on a aeroplane? Or seen one?"

I shook my head, "No, I haven't." He pulled up into this huge car park in front of us, was this strange building with like antennas sticking up all over it, as I was staring at the building a plane took off behind it.

"Jump out, Danielle, your in for a treat." I followed him into the building which was vast, we went over to a kiosk where he brought us both a drink. "Come look at this, Danielle." He led me to a huge window which covered the entire wall, in front of it were wooden benches that we sat on. Through the window we could see at least ten aeroplanes, all different colours and sizes. One of them was being towed by some sort of truck, and there was a luggage cart making its way to one of the waiting aeroplanes. "Danielle, look over there. One's about to take off." There appeared to be so much activity I couldn't make out where he meant, but suddenly an aeroplane was tearing down the runway my dad was getting really excited. "Look! Danielle, look! It will be up in the air at any moment." I kept my eyes totally focused on the aeroplane. It was gaining speed, getting faster and faster; it was getting to the end of the runway and I was holding my breath, wondering what happens then. Gracefully, like a giant bird, it started to rise, floating around three feet of the ground, we were both totally transfixed by it as it took to the the sky, we watched it until it was completely out of sight.

We spent a good few hours at the airport watching the aeroplanes. It was fascinating, my dad was telling me the different types, where they were going. I saw the holiday makers happily boarding their planes, and the returning ones all tanned departing theirs; I could envisage what it could possibly be like floating through the air in one of those huge aircrafts. "One day, Danielle, no doubt you will get to go up in one of those and experience it for yourself."

There is no way I could ever see that happening. "I doubt it Dad." Arr I had called him Dad. He had realised and, smiling down at me, replyied, "Come on daughter, let's get some food. I don't know about you, but I am ravinous."

Getting back in the car, I watched out for the last sightings of a departing or returning airplane, and pointed them out to my dad as he drove. We arrived at a chip shop, it was a take away or you could eat in. I took a seat and my dad placed our order. This was much better than some fancy restaurant; I couldn't really go wrong ordering sausage, chips and a bottle of pop, and I had been to the toilet in the airport so there was no fear of me getting locked in again. We chatted while we ate, my dad instigating the topics of conversation. After he dropped me back off at home, he explained he was going to be working away for a few weeks but not to worry he would be over to see me again the first weekend he had free.

My mum was watching television when I got back, another wildlife programme. I did not like them, watching a pack of lions rip up a poor zebra or whatever to pieces, was not my idea of entertainment, I just could not stomach the goriness of it. So our conversation would have to wait, but I was determined I was going to ask her, but now was not the time. "Mum, I won't be seeing him for a couple of weeks as he is working away." I don't think she even registered I was speaking to her, as she had her eyes glued to the sickening sight on the television.

16

The following week I was proved correct, she had not been listening or paying any attention to what had been said when she told me to go get ready, as my dad would be along for me. Sighing, I explained to her what he had said about being away. She looked put out as if it was interfering with her plans in some way, "Mum, why did you tell me my dad was dead?" She gave me the look which meant don't push it.

"Danielle, I told you he was dead, because he has never bothered with you, he has never paid a penny to your upkeep, and I felt it was easier if I simply told you he was dead, that way you wouldn't feel rejected by your own father."

"OK I guess that makes sense, so why is he bothering now?"

"I don't know, you will have to ask him that, I just hope he doesn't let you down, Danielle."

As I was now at a loose end with not going out with my dad, I decided to do some school work at the dining room table. My mum was busying herself making a casserole in the kitchen. After about an hour there was a knock at the door. My mum looked slightly embarrassed as she opened the door as standing there were a couple of coal delivery men – bizarre to say the very least as it was a Sunday. There they were though blackened up in their work clothes, the one at the door chatting to my mum while his work mate emptied sack after sack into our coal house. "Ryan you giving us a hand or what?" Giving my mum a broad grin, Ryan as I now knew him set to helping deliver the rest of the load.

"Danielle, get that table cleared of your school stuff, dinner's ready." Doing as instructed and setting the table for two, my mum came in with an extra dish, followed by Ryan in his filthy clothes. "We have company for dinner today, as there is plenty. I have asked him to have some with us." I sat at the table slowly eating my food, watching them exchanging glances but not really saying much. Ryan ate his casserole as if he had not ate for a week and then had seconds, saying it was yummy when he had done. He was a big man – and by this I mean fat – with jet-black hair combed back off his face in the style of Elvis Presley. He was around 5foot 10inch in height and I figured that even though he appeared fat he must be strong as it can be no mean feat humping coal sacks around all day. He left as soon as he had finished saying, "There would be another delivery the same time next month."

Which there was, and it was the same thing. Mum would cook her casserole, he would eat a couple of bowls, thank her and leave, after a while it became normal. Jerry was never at home, it would just be the three of us, but I never thought anything of it. After one of his visits Jerry came home and was tucking into his casserole. "Laura, this is lovely, it is really good."

With out thinking I responded. "I know, the coal man enjoyed it too." My mum's face was a picture, Jerry literally dropped his spoon in his casserole. "What the hell, does she mean by that?" Jerry yelled at my mum, it was the first time ever I had seen my mum lost for words, she was literally stuttering and tripping up over her words. Jerry looked exasperated, pushing back his chair as he stood up with that much force that it fell backwards, tumbling across the floor. "Sod this, I'm back off out." He went to the back door nearly slamming it of its hinges as he went through it.

My mum just stood in the middle of the room, glaring at me, I didn't know how to respond, because as far as I could see I had done nothing wrong I had simply spoke the truth. "Danielle, why did you have to say that? Now look at all the trouble you have caused." She was livid with me, she was actually spitting the words out at me. Now it was my turn to be stuck for words, so I simply shrugged, as I had no response I was not going to apologise for telling the truth. For the rest of the day she was slamming stuff about in temper and muttering under her breath, it was a relief when it was finally bed time.

The next day, there was no sign of Jerry, but it was obvious he had been back from the corker of a black eye my mum was now wearing. I couldn't look at her, I kept my head down while eating breakfast as to avoid eye contact. I was feeling guilty it was my fault he had hit her. Me and my big mouth, why did I have to say what I said. Now there was no taking it back, it was out there. It was strange, because though they were obviously having blazing rows while I was in bed, I never heard them only saw the evidence the next day on my mum. I had, due to the reaction of Jerry, started to wonder if something was going on between her and Ryan, something I had not even considered, while Ryan had been sat at our dining room table tucking into his monthly casseroles. Which explains why I probably said what I said on that fateful day, as I thought it was all innocent, obviously something Jerry did not agree on, due to his reaction, and the bruises on my mum.

Jerry was away from home a lot in the day, which suited me fine as I could not stand him, but it was obvious when he had been home in an evening by the state of my mum's poor face. No sooner had the damage healed than she was battered again. Coming down for breakfast one morning I was agasp at the state of her, not usually saying anything as it was an awkward thing to comment on that morning was an exception. "Oh my god! Mum, what the hell has he done?" You could hardly see her face it was awash with bruise upon bruise.

"I would say that's pretty obvious," she replied. Even though I was only nine and scared of him, I wanted to give him a piece of my mind

"Where is he?" I demanded.

"He's not here, Danielle." I was not giving up, so I asked again.

"OK, OK, if you must know he has been locked up for the night, pending charges." My mouth dropped agape as I took in this new information. Arrested – crikey my mum had finally had enough, hopefully he was gone for good.

17

I went to school as normal, but could not really focus on any of my studies, as I was wondering what was happening back home. On my return my mum was still in; she had not gone into work, but called in sick. "Danielle, I have to go down to the police station, I won't be long, I promise."

I asked her why? She responded by saying that she needed to drop the charges against Jerry, and that hopefully a night inside would pull him into line. Oh no, she had to be kidding, surely. Why would she want him anywhere near her after the beatings she had took. She put on her coat and virtually ran out, saying she had to get a move on, that there was a deadline, and if she didn't make it he would be spending another night behind bars. I hated him, he could rot in there for all I cared.

Jerry never returned home with her, and I was left wondering if she had done what she had said, or if she had met up with Ryan, who would surely be gunning for Jerry once he saw the state she was in. Her face during the day had puffed up even more, her eyes looked shut from all the bruising, her lip had split from the swelling and one side of her face appeared uneven to the other. I wasn't sure if it was from all the bruising or if he had actually broke her cheekbone on one side. Personally I would not have gone out the door looking like that, but I guess my mum had got used to it over the years, and maybe even carried her injuries as a sign of resilience, and was not bothered who saw her, or was just past caring.

My mum had Jerry arrested half a dozen times after that if not more. It was always the same story: he would batter her, she would have him done for it, and then she would drop the charges, and he would be released. In the end the police had enough, and had built up enough evidence against him, so that the final time my mum went running to them for help after another beating, they arrested him as normal, but when she went down yet again to drop the charges, they refused to release him. My mum was beside herself she didn't know what to do, or what the outcome would be for her once he was let out, she was a nervous wreck. "Oh god, Danielle, what have I done? I should never have gone to them in the first place, it is all my fault." Obviously I had no sympathy for him, and hoped he would be banged up for a long time, but sadly he wasn't, I don't know the outcome, but I know he went to court and was found guilty of asault and battery.

On his release, Jerry again was not around much, he would come home after work have his dinner my mum had prepared, and then go straight out again. It was tense at home, but he never appeared to hit her again or if he did it was not anything you could see as in facial injuries. My mum was bitter towards him saying, "He was nothing but a pervert with his filthy porn mags. He thinks we know nothing about the ones hidden under the sofa." This was the first I knew about any of this, and being an inquisitive nine year old it was obvious that at the first opportunity I was going to check this new information out. So as soon as my mum left the house I was rooting under the sofa looking for the magazines, how I wished I had kept well away. Pulling magazine after magazine out from under the sofa, there must have been around sixty of the things, I had never seen anything like it in my life, I could not even find words to describe what I was looking at.

I never opened any of the magazines, I just sat there totally shocked by the images on the front covers. Everyone was different, but were the same in a bizarre way; they were all pictures of naked girls and women in various stances, a few had women and naked men on the covers performing different sex acts. They made me feel sick to the stomach to look at, and I wished my mum had never said anything, just glancing at them was enough to turn my stomach, I could not believe people would lower themselves to do this, for perverts like my so-called step dad to perv over.

I hurriedly pushed them back under the sofa, wishing I knew nothing about their sordid existence. I sat on the sofa trying to take in what I had seen, but then again trying to erase the images from my mind but no matter how hard I tried the filthy images stuck like glue. In the end I could not even bear being sat on the sofa, as it made me feel filthy and sordid, so I sat on a chair opposite glaring at the sofa willing it to burst into flames or the stuff under it just to evaporate.

It was awkward when Jerry came home for dinner that evening; I could not stand to look at him, never mind make pleasantries or small talk. I had the image of him in my head of the morning he came into my room stark naked. It had not felt right at the time, it felt like something he should not have been doing, or I should have been seeing. I was also wondering if he would know I had seen his magazines, that they had obviously been tampered with and were out of order, that's if he kept them in some kind of order. You know new edition, favourite – the very thought of it made me blush and shudder inside. Well, I would just have to wait and see if there was going to be any consequences from my childish curiosity. Thankfully after dinner he went out as per usual, he was all dressed up, stinking of the aftershave of the time – old spice I think, or something similar. He smelt like he had bathed in it, it was that pungent.

18

My dad kept his word, and a few weeks after our trip to the airport he was back to take me out. I was excitedly waiting on the front as his car pulled up, my face dropped as I saw he was not alone. Sat in the front passenger seat was Maureen. *Oh no what is she doing here?* I wanted my dad to myself, this wasn't fair. My dad held the car door open for me as usual as I climbed in. "We're going to the coast today, Danielle, and as it's such a long way, I have asked Maureen to join us." Maureen turned round in her seat and smiled at me, but I did not respond. I didn't want her here I wanted it to be just me and my dad.

Halfway to the coast we pulled into a service station for a toilet break and a drink; there had hardly been two words spoken between any of us on the first part of our journey. I was obviously sulking, and any conversation my dad tried to engage in with me simply got a yes or no response. Maureen spoke a little but in hushed tones to my dad, but sitting in the back I could not make out what was being said between them and to be honest I didn't care.

It was an odd day to be going to the coast; it was the beginning of November and the weather was bleak, windy and cold. My dads car was nice and warm, but as soon as you stepped out it made you shudder, and you just wanted to get back in his car as quickly as you could. After our tea break we proceeded to the coast. I would have been happy for my dad to turn the car round there and then and take me back home. It was not the same Maureen being there with us, and she never spoke two words to me so what was the point her even being here.

The second part of the journey as the first was in partial silence; I kept looking at my dad through his visor mirror, and he would wink back at me and make me giggle. "Right we're here. Jump out, Danielle, and just climb over that dune and you will see the sea," my dad announced, I looked out the car window where I was settled and warm. The wind was that strong it was whipping the tops of the trees from side to side. The sand on the dunes was swirling around and looked like it was doing its own ritual dance, with the grasses being blown from side to side with such force, it was literally whipping them out the ground.

I shuddered and wrapped my coat tighter around me, there was no way I was getting out the car. Litter in a nearby litter bin was suddenly lifted out the bin and was clattering down the road. *Oh my god are these people crazy wanting to get out in this?* Maureen was the first to brave it, with my dad slowly following her; their hair was getting blown all over, and Maureen's scarf no matter how many times she tucked it back in her coat was blown out a second later. They turned to me and waved to me to get out the car, I simply shook my head – there was no way I was getting out. They walked a little down the road but never braved climbing the dune to see the sea, and after a few minutes dithering returned back to the car. My dad nearly lost the car door as he opened it as the force of the wind nearly caused him to lose his grasp on it.

Their cheeks were glowing when they resettled themselves back in their seats. "My word it's parky out there, lass, I can't blame you for not getting out, I nearly lost my footing, and followed that litter down the street," he laughed. Maureen mentioned lunch, so on the way back we called into a restaurant; this time I was handed a menu, but, glancing at it not sure again what to chose, Maureen pointed out a children's menu.

The restaurant was warm and inviting after being sat so long in the car. It was not busy and we were soon served. I had ordered fish fingers and chips off the children's section. It felt more comfortable sat in there and my dad and Maureen were chatting. They told me Maureen had two daughters and two sons, and the next time we went out I would be introduced to them. They explained they were all older than me but not by much, and that they knew all about me and were excited to meet me. My dad said that no matter what, I would always be his little girl that there was only one Danielle Margaret Foster. I nearly choked on my drink: Danielle Margaret Foster that was not my name, my name was Danielle Margaret Jackson.

My dad shot off his chair and slapped me on the back laughing, "I don't know, Danielle, that's what you get for drinking so fast." Tears were running down my cheeks, from the force of the pop going down the wrong way, and I could barely speak. "No it's not that, Dad," I spluttered, and I was on the verge of telling them about my name, and then remembered the incident with Ryan and how I had spoke out and the trouble it had caused, so quickly added, "Yes you are right I should be more careful."

When I was dropped off at home I ran in to ask my mum why my name was different to my dad's. She sighed, then went on to explain that it had been easier to call me by Jerry's surname, as I was so young when they had got married it was easier if we were all called the same. Not really understanding she went on to explain, that when I was enrolled for school, and she was faced with the paperwork she figured it would make life better for me at school if all our surnames were the same. She also said that all my records were in the name of Jackson doctors, hospital and school it saved confusion, but on my birth certificate it was clearly stated my name is Danielle Margaret Foster.

I was not sure how much more I could take. Since turning nine, my dad had appeared from the grave; my mum had obviously taken up with some new guy, that I had been unknowingly a part of; I had four possible step brothers and sisters I never knew anything about; Dawn had tried to cave my head in with a brick; my mum was being constantly attacked by my stepdad, who had been in and out of jail; I had found out he was some sex pervert due to his sickening magazine collection; and now my name was not my name. My head was spinning, I felt like I was on some kind of crazy roller coaster that just never ended, and I just could not get off.

19

I was struggling with all this overload of information, I could find no reason or meaning to any of it, it was just madness. If I needed or wanted to talk there was only my mum, and I didn't want to keep raking stuff up, as she was dealing with her own stuff, plus she was never a sympathetic or loving parent. I found myself wishing, we lived up north near my grandparents and aunts so I could have someone impartial to confide in, but then again would I, or would I feel I was betraying my mum? After all she was the only one there for me.

I didn't know what to do with all this pent up emotion, I started to swear as a way to get some release, obviously not in front of my mum or Jerry, but when I was with my school mates, or playing out I would swear like a trooper, stringing one swear word on to another, trying to get all the venom I felt out of my system. It obviously did not work, I still had all this hurt and anxiety building up inside of me, but for a few seconds it helped.

After school a few friends had come back with me to my house. My mum and Jerry were out so it didn't matter, and we were only messing about in the garden. I had found an old rusted hammer and was venting my temper on a few bits of rubble scattered on the floor. The others were entertaining themselves with different activities: the boys were hunting under stones and rocks for worms and bugs and the youngest of us was singing nursery rhymes to her doll.

I raised the hammer thinking, *Right, I am going to smash you into a thousand pieces.* Slamming the hammer down, I missed the rubble and the hammer came smashing down on my hand. "Fucking hell, you bastard thing." The words were no sooner out of my mouth than a voice thundered across the garden: "Danielle, get here. I'll teach you once and for all to come out with that filth." Everybody froze and turned at once. It was Jerry; he looked furious. "Danielle," he roared "don't let me have to tell you twice." Shaking I made my way towards him, I knew this was not going to end well, and I was embarrassed that my friends were going to witness my fate.

He flung open the outside toilet door – oh no I really did not want my friends to witness this. He went to grab my arm but I gave him the slip, so he grabbed me around the waist, forcing me into the toilet. "Get here, you little brat, you'll never swear again once I'm done with you." Turning me upside down I knew what was coming. As he lowered me into the toilet I managed to spread my hands on the toilet seat so he had to force me in. I could feel my arms buckle and as I went down I managed to get a glance of the three children stood watching outside the toilet door. There was a scream from the youngest girl, who could not bear to watch and who had gone running back to her parents screaming at the top of her voice.

The shock of hearing her screams stopped Jerry in his tracks and he placed me back on my feet, he appeared stunned there were other people present and looked visibly flustered, obviously he had been focusing on me, and probably not been aware the other children were even there. Nearly knocking the two boys aside he muttered, "Danielle, go back and play." Feeling totally humiliated I went back up the garden, with the two boys following me. One of them came over and asked if I was OK? And who the man was. Shaking and through floods of tears I explained he was my stepdad. The boy put his arm round me and said, "You poor sod, what an evil man."

A few days later my mum and Jerry, were walking down our street. I saw them, so ran up to meet them, but as I got to them a man came flying out his door, making a bee line for us. "You, I have been watching out for you," we all froze as he headed straight for Jerry. "You call yourself a man? Terrorizing a small child, and not any child may I add, but my daughter. She came in the other day screaming and in tears at what she experienced, and has not slept properly since."

Jerry instantly flushed up stammering, for his words. "Danielle, here take the key, and run along." It was my mum. I took the key she offered and slowly ran down the road. Jerry had still not found his voice and as I glanced back, I could see the man had a hold of Jerry by his shirt collar and was ranting into his face, looking like he would punch him out if he made one move. From where I was, I could not make out what was being said, but it looked serious. My mum was stood about three feet away looking puzzled by the whole situation, and was looking nervously around to see if anyone was witnessing the commotion.

I figured it was the little girl's dad protecting his little princess. When my mum and Jerry got in a few moments later my mum looked over at me with curiosity on her face. "You alright, Danielle, is there anything you need to tell me?" Jerry was stood fidgeting behind her, not making any eye contact with any of us.

"No mum, why?" she glared back at Jerry who made a hasty retreat upstairs.

20

A few days after, I was in the back garden when my mum rushed out the house. "Danielle, come here quick, and be quiet," she ushered me into the outside coal house. "Now stay there, Danielle, and don't make a sound and whatever happens don't come out." She closed the door on me it was pitch black in there and smelt fusty and damp, there was a small trickle of light coming through the keyhole so I squinted through it so I could see what was happening outside.

My dad suddenly appeared, and my mum was talking to him in a low voice, but no matter how hard I tried I was unable to make out what was being said. My mum appeared to be doing most of the talking, and my dad appeared shaken by whatever was being said. How I wish I could hear what was going on. My mum glanced over to the coal house as if checking I had stayed put. My dad, shaking his head, turned around and left. I stood there waiting to be released, but she turned around and went back indoors.

I stood there in that coal house probably ten minutes after he left but it felt like an age. I looked behind me; it was pitch black I didn't know where the coal lay so I did not dare move from the spot I was in. I had visions of spiders and creepy crawlies, and the air in there was thick and damp; it was starting to make me gasp for air. What was wrong with her, why wasn't she letting me out? Was she leaving me in here all day or what? Finally I saw her come out the back door and walk towards the coal house, opening the door to let me out. I instantly choked and gasped as my lungs filled with the clean air. "Danielle, go to your bedroom and read a book." I did not argue I was just relieved to be free.

Puzzled, I chose a book and was flicking through the pages, when there was a knock on my bedroom door. It was my dad. "Hi, Danielle, can I come in?" Surprised to see him especially in the house, I nodded. He sat on the bed at the side of me and told me that I would not be seeing him again. He handed me a piece of paper saying it was his phone number, and if I ever needed anything to call him. I looked at him and the paper and could not find a response, I was totally shocked. I had no idea how to use a phone, mind make a call, we had no phone, and I had no money to use a phone box plus I was probably to small to reach the phone if I had. "I am off now, Danielle, and don't forget if you need me just call." I watched him leave the room, and I did not budge from where I sat I was totally stunned. I slowly opened the paper he gave me and saw his number. I felt like ripping it up there and then, but instead I scanned my room for a suitable safe place, finally settling on putting it in my pencil case.

I just could not get my head around what had happened, why would he say such a thing? Surely he did not mean it. It made no sense, no sense at all. We seemed to get on well, I always behaved when he took me out. Why turn up in my life? Why make contact with his only daughter just to walk away? No he did not mean it, he was only messing surely.

That week at school I could not get it out of my mind questions going round and round in my head. I was quiet at school, quiet at home just staying in my room. I had started to get feelings for my dad, I was a little girl craving attention and I was getting a little off my dad, and now he was gone and all I had left of him was a scrap of paper as a reminder.

On the Saturday morning, my mum told me to go get smartened up and wait on the front as my dad was picking me up. I instantly had a great big beam on my face and ran upstairs to get ready. I chose my best dress, I put on my special coat, and sat patiently on the front kerb waiting for my dad to show. For every car that turned the corner of our street, I would jump up excitedly, expecting to see his car. After what seemed an age I started to become deflated; it was November and it was bitterly cold. My coat was not keeping me warm and my bum was going numb from the cold pavement – where was he? I would give him ten minutes more then I would have to go in. Finally I had to accept defeat. He was not coming, he was playing some kind of sick game; probably thought it was funny to have his daughter freeze to death, waiting on him, knowing all along he was not going to show up.

Shaking from the cold I went back in. "You're back quick, what happened?"

Bursting into tears I told her: "He never turned up."

"Oh Danielle, I knew he would let you down. You're better of just forgetting about him." How was I meant to do that? I went in the front room watching the traffic going up and down the road for hours, willing my dad's car to suddenly stop outside, but of course it didn't. I was absolutely gutted, why would he do this to me? I hated him. My mum was right, I didn't need him; he had come into my life turned it upside down and then just turned around and left.

21

I spent a lot of time at that front room window, weekend after weekend, watching the cars going up and down willing, praying that my dad's would pull up outside and things would return to normal. The first weekend after he left was the worst; I spent hours sat there looking out, wondering what I had done to make him go away? Why he didn't want to know me anymore? Tears were burning my cheeks as they poured down my face. I could not understand any of it why? Why? Why was he treating me like this? I wanted to hate him but I couldn't, he was the man that had taken me out in his car before then I had never been in a proper car a taxi but that's not the same. He was the man who had treated me to new clothes, meals and new experiences. I was incapable of hating him, I simply felt rejected and hurt by him. I had started to get real feelings for him, and I believed he felt the same. He appeared pleased to see me when we went out, and yet now this, I also felt jealous I had not had chance to meet my stepbrothers and sisters but I was jealous of them, jealous that they had him, and I did not – I was stuck with Jerry. He was my real dad not theirs, so what was the justice in that? It stunk, and yet he had passed me over like an abandoned pup to go back to his perfect life, with his perfect cerealbox family.

"Danielle, you can't sit there all day, what are you looking for?"

Turning round to face her, my cheeks still damp from the tears and my eyes blood shot I replied, "I am just watching the traffic, Mum." Sighing she left the room. "Danielle, he is not coming back. You just need to get used to it, he has gone." I knew she was right, he had told me as much. Dragging myself from the window I went to my room to retrieve his phone number from my pencil case. I stared at it for ages as if somehow it held all the answers to my present situation. I scanned the room looking for a safer hiding place for the scrap of paper as it was getting overly creased in the pencil case. In my windowsil was a small jewellery box. On opening it up there was a piece of mesh fabric in the bottom so taking it out I folded the paper as small as I could, and laid it in the box, carefully replacing the mesh on top. Finally satisfied the number was safe I took a sigh of relief. I would probably never use it, but it was the last thing I had of my dad, so I wanted to keep it safe and away from prying eyes. My mum never asked me about my dad's visit to my room, so I had not told her about the phone number. It felt like a secret just between me and my dad.

School was gearing up for Christmas, so I had things to keep me busy. At school the school nativity, making Christmas decorations for the tree in the school hall, and chains for the endless school corridors, but my dad was never far from my thoughts. Our teacher had us making our own Christmas cards and homemade presents, it was a lot of fun. On our final day it was toy day no school work. All the class were allowed to bring in one toy or game, and we also had our Christmas party. Everyone had brought in a small amount of food to contribute and of course no Christmas party's complete without a visit from Santa Claus. We all patiently lined up to see him and was presented with a selection box each. I was now of an age where I was doubting the true presence of Santa Claus, I still wanted to believe as it was so magical, but then again the other children were saying it was their parents etc. so I had to wonder. I know which I would have preferred it to be though. The thought of a man in a red coat, with a sack full of gifts climbing down a chimney – who wouldn't want to rather believe in that?

My mum did do a few decorations at Christmas. We had a four-foot tree sat on a coffee table – and there was an angel on the top. I had made some chains at school for the ceiling and we had two different coloured balloons in each corner of the room. It did look cheery. The Christmas cards we had received were hanging above the fire on two lengths of string, secured by drawing pins at either end. My mum always put on a nice spread at Christmas. She made time to bake, making her own mince pies, sausage rolls and fairy cakes. I used to always hang around while she baked hoping to be offered the mixing bowl the fairy cakes had been mixed in. I would have loved to have helped her, but she was always in a rush to get it done, so I just used to watch on the side lines grateful for the bowl at the end.

On Christmas morning, like every other child in the land, I was downstairs at the crack of dawn excited to see what Santa had left me. On the chimney breast hung a long sock. I rushed over to empty it out and sighed, as the usual yearly orange, apple, nuts and a bottle of bubbles fell out. I had to smile: this was the only time of year we had a fruit bowl out, and as I looked over at it was left wondering if the apple and orange had been nestled on the top of the others the night before.

There was a pile of gifts on the small table under the tree. I had not asked, or been asked, what I would like for Christmas so had no idea what to expect as I unwrapped them. The first one was a Enid Blyton book, *The Famous Five*, then a Christmas stocking full of a selection of different chocolates – yummy – a spinning top, pyjamas and finally a compendium of games in a box, consisting of snakes and ladders, ludo etc. It was still early, too early to wake anyone up so I went into the kitchen to get a drink, and in there stood up against the kitchen counters was a beautiful, shiny scooter – wow, I loved it. As I stood admiring it my mum walked in. "Merry Christmas, Danielle, looks like you must have been a very good girl this year!"

We had a great Christmas day I was allowed to stuff myself silly with the chocolate out of my Christmas stocking. There was only the three of us for dinner, and obviously

I was unable to eat hardly any of it after stuffing myself with chocolates but and wasn't a cross word from either of them. After we watched the Queen's speech, which my mum insisted on every year, followed by the Christmas movie; then she laid on a small buffet that we could help ourselves to off and on all evening. We played with my new games, even Jerry joined in. That night I went to bed happy and slept soundly for once.

22

I spent all the rest of the Christmas holidays on my scooter, I loved it. I was lucky we lived at the top of a steep hill so I would have one leg on the scooter and the other on the pavement and run as fast as I could, as soon as I got the speed up, I would take my foot off the pavement and sail down the street giggling all the way, with the wind blowing through my hair. There was not much traffic on our street, no one could really afford a car, so it was very rare a car came up our street. The council had made it one-way traffic so I was perfectly safe bombing up and down. I was no sooner at the bottom of the hill than I would go running back up to the top to do it all again, it made me feel free and gave me some kind of strange release. I simply loved my new toy.

At New Year Jerry and my mum went out, leaving me in with a selection of treats and drinks, telling me they were going to see the new year in at the local pub and they would see me when they got in if I was still up. Glancing at the clock it was 7pm it was another five hours before the new year. I had spent a good few hours tearing up and down on my scooter and was feeling weary; I honestly was not expecting to still be up when they returned. By eight o'clock I was beat so went upstairs had a quick bath and settled into bed. I could hear people outside making their way to the pub or a party, excitedly chatting as they passed. I soon drifted off, to be woken by Jerry and my mum coming in obviously the worse for wear and bickering over something or the other. Wiping the sleep out of my eyes I went downstairs. Jerry was stood on the doorstep looking puzzled while my mum was refusing to let him in. "No, no you can't come in yet you've not got your lump of coal, and you need soap, whiskey and a candle." Seeing me coming downstairs she turned to face me. "Danielle, quick, go in the bathroom and get the soap." By the time I retrieved the soap Jerry was stood on the front step dithering, with the coal and other items my mum had insisted on in his hands. "Right you can come in now, Jerry," she said, passing him the soap.

"What are you doing?" I asked.

"It's a northern tradition: a dark haired man is meant to be your first male visitor to pass the threshhold after New Year's Eve, bringing a candle for light, coal for heat, soap for cleanliness and liquor so you don't go thirsty all year." This was a new tradition to me, I had never ever heard of it and by the look on Jerry's face neither had he. There was only one flaw with this and that was the fact Jerry was not dark, he was without a question of a doubt ginger-haired.

The rest of the school year was relatively quiet, and thankfully I never had any more run ins with Debra and apart from Jerry deciding I was his personal remote control for the television, as he could not be bothered to get up and change the channels himself, I was pretty much left alone. About two months before I was about to break up for the school holidays, my mum came in all excited. "Danielle, have you seen the new pet shop down the road? They have the cutest kittens in the window. They're a Siamese cross and they have bright blue eyes – they're gorgeous. Would you like one?" Well a cat's not something I had been considering, if I was honest, but my mum was full of it and could not wait to show them off to me in the pet shop window. "Oh look, Danielle, aren't they gorgeous? Which one would you choose?" I looked at the kittens through the shop window but felt nothing, I did not think they were particularly cute, but my mum kept insisting and in the end I pointed to the one nearest to us. "Come on, Danielle, let's see if you have picked a boy or girl." To be honest I couldn't care less; they all looked the same to me. In the shop the owner turned the poor thing upside down and announced we were now the proud owners of a tom cat.

Carrying the kitten back home in a cardboard box with a few air holes punched in. We could hear him meowing he did not sound happy about the prospect of a new home. "So what are you going to call him?" Mum asked.

"I don't know," I replied. The fact was, it was still sinking in from nowhere I was now the owner of a kitten I wasn't that fussed about. Placing him carefully on the kitchen floor my mum told me to release him to see what he would do, as the flaps on the box were opened he tumbled out running straight behind the twin tub. There was no way we could get him out. As I tried to grab him he would shrink further back out of my grasp. In the end we left him to settle as he appeared absolutely petrified of us. He spent a good hour wedged behind the twin tub, in the end we had to pull it out and I managed to get him as he raced to his next bolt hole. As I held him he was shaking like a leaf. Arr the poor thing. After a few minutes he settled and curled up on my lap and fell asleep: I did not dare move in case he fled again. Looking down at him properly for the first time he appeared all vulnerable and alone. My heart started to melt. *OK then I guess you are cute.* He opened his eyes and looked up at me with the brightest blue eyes I had ever seen. His fur was pure black and as glossy as silk, *OK little man you're a keeper.* "Mum, I am going to call him Sooty." Yawning Sooty crawled up to my neck and nuzzled in purring and drifted back off to sleep, finally content.

23

Jerry on his arrival home was not as impressed with the new addition, and shooed him away every time he went near him. Sooty, my mum decided, was going to be an outside cat, so after a month the poor thing was booted out night after night. As Jerry was not keen on him he left him out in the day, so on my return from school he would be waiting for me on the front door step waiting to be let in for a few hours before being put out again.

One morning he came in battered and bruised; he had scratches and bites all over him, so he had obviously had a run in with another local cat. This gave him a little respite as he was allowed to recover indoors for a few weeks, he was such a loving cat, he would curl up at the side of me and purr away in his sleep obviously exhausted from all his outdoor antics. Jerry never warmed to Sooty and his scratching on the chair legs infuriated him, to the point he slung him across the room at my mum, he seemed to hang in the air for ages before luckily being caught by her just before hitting the living room wall. I hated Jerry; he was now persecuting a poor defenceless animal. Was there no end to his nastiness.

The summer holiday was spent as usual with my grandparents up north. Darren was now a regular visitor too in the holiday, but he always only stayed a few weeks before being picked up by his parents. We were getting on better; I didn't see him as a threat anymore and he had outgrown my special bear so I had him back though he still felt tarnished and soiled. Darren had returned home before my birthday and it was nice to have my aunts and grandparents to myself on my special day.

I opened all my birthday cards in a rush, tearing each envelope open as fast as I could, looking for the one from my dad, but he had not sent me one. I flung the cards down in a huff, and had the same emotions running through me of rejection and loss. So he had meant it, he was really gone. This had been my last hope that little light in the darkness to show me that he did care and that I was important to him, but obviously I wasn't, not even worth the price of a card or a stamp. I decided there and then I was done with him. I was not going to waste anymore time or energy focusing on where he was, what he was doing, if he was thinking about me, as now I had my answer. Obviously he was not thinking of me. If he could not even remember his only child's birthday, stuff him – he was not worth my time.

This was my last year at primary school, which entailed us all taking our eleven plus to determine if we were going to the local secondary, or if we passed, the grammar school.

We were all under a lot of pressure to work hard and achieve our full potential, being given endless homework and assignments to complete. I was determined to do well and work hard to get to the grammar school. My mum never put any pressure on me, and never really seemed that interested in my school work. I got the usual "No television until your homework's done", but she never checked if it was done or not, or asked if I needed any assistance. I was just left to get on with it. The school justified all this extra work, saying it would put us in good stead for when we all moved on, because then we would really know how hard homework was.

Coming home from school loaded down with books for my next assignment, I found my mum in. She was tearful and upset. She had a glass at the side of her with possibly sherry in, but I was not sure, but I knew it was alcoholic. As I walked in she glared at me, I knew instinctively not to say anything and just go to my room. "Danielle, you know your dad, he is a wicked man. That woman he is now married to, he was carrying on with her while I was pregnant with you. I can remember the day as clearly as anything: I was sat in a chair knitting you some booties, and he stood right in front of me and told me he was leaving us for her, her and her four brats." Jestering with her hands she stood up staggering. "The needles I was holding in my hands I plunged into him, into his arm." She was doing the motions through the air of needles being plunged deep into someone's arm. "Danielle, he left us both, never looked back just went off with her. It caused me to have a complete mental break down, and you need to know that you were born in that *mental hospital*."

I stood looking at my mum in total amazement, I was born in a *mental hospital*, the words were spinning around and around in my head "a *mental hospital*, a *mental hospital*". In that moment it felt like my entire world had just caved in and I had a total loathing for my dad. I did not care if I never saw him again, I did not want to see him again ever, not as long as I lived. My mum had collapsed back into her chair and was silently sobbing; I could not go and comfort her, I was in total shock. I needed to get out of there, I needed to escape.

I ran out of the house and to the only place I felt safe: the park at the top of our road. I needed air I needed to clear my head. Everything in my mind was jumbled, and I was struggling to process this new information. I sat on the park bench looking at the horizon but not really taking it in, just sat there looking out to space. Why did this stuff keep happening to me? I was born in a mental hospital I knew it was true by the state my mum had been in. Christ if this was ever to get out I would be mortified, I would never live it down. I wanted to die, or the ground to simply swallow me up right there and then. I looked down at my hands they were visibly shaking, in fact every inch of me was shaking. It was then I realised how cold it was, the wind was howling around me I could feel the ice in the air, I did not want to go back home, I wanted to go anywhere but there. I continued to sit lost in my own thoughts, I was scared to go home, I did not want to hear anymore, anymore of my messed up life, but the icy wind had got the better of me so crying I returned home.

24

Somehow I managed to keep it together, I never mentioned a word of what my mum had said to anyone, how could I, I would be a laughing stock. It would have given Dawn the ultimate weapon to beat me with, without laying a single finger on me. I had lost my spark though, I was totally squashed. It felt like I had taken an emotional beating. My mum thankfully never mentioned it again, but it remained with me like a black stain on my heart, it made me feel worthless and miserable. I would burst into tears at the simplest things, and not have the strength to retaliate when the children at school teased or taunted me.

I tried to focus on my studies and assignments as a distraction, but it was hard I could not shake it out of my head, I wish she had never told me especially now, when it was such an important academic year. It was only a few weeks and I would be sitting the eleven plus, the school were making a big deal of it. So I knew it was important to do well.

When the day finally came, we were put on individual tables in our classroom, spaced out so we could not cheat or glance at another class mates answers. "Right, class you have one hour from now, so turn over your papers and begin," said the teacher. Apprehensively turning the paper over I glanced down at the first question, taking a sigh of relief I answered it easily and the next ten questions without a pause. *OK I can do this, it's not as bad as I thought it would be.*

Suddenly the classroom door opened and another teacher walked in, followed by a line of students. "Oh I am so sorry about this, but their teachers been taken ill, so they're going to have to sit in here until we sort something." Glancing round I saw the line of children, roughly about ten of them, but the one that made my heart sink was Dawn lined up with the others staring straight over at me. "OK, children, go find a seat, but you need to be quiet," my teacher announced. Dawn immediately came over to where I was, and pulled out the chair at the side of me, she was smiling. "Hi Danielle, you OK? What yer doing?" Looking away from my work I told her that it was an exam, the eleven plus. Trying to refocus she carried on chatting putting me off the task at hand. I did not dare not respond to her, I was scared of her, and before I knew it the hour was up and I had not even turned the page to the next set of questions.

Damn, why had she had to come into our class today of all days? She had totally messed up my chances of going to the grammar school, but I could not just blame her: it was her and the school's fault. Why had her teacher had to go off sick on this day, on one of the most important days of my life? I would seem like a complete failure, when my papers were marked, well the one page of it that is. I had spent all that time, all that hard work preparing for this exam, and now it was wasted, wasted by a series of circumstances out of my control. As predicted I failed the exam and would be going to be attending the local secondary school after the summer holidays, the other children who had passed were delighting in their achievement but I felt cheated of my rightful place.

Jerry was less and less at home, and my mum had started always having a glass at the side of her as a companion. Most days she was drunk, and when she got drunk she got nasty, raking up the past calling my dad every name from a dog to a pig. She was pulling me down with her nasty comments and criticisms. On one of these days she told me that Jerry was seeing another woman, and that the next day they were going to the cinema together and we would be there to catch him in the act. I did not think much of it and just put it down to the rantings of a drunk, but sure enough the next day I was ordered to put on my best attire as we were going to the cinema.

I had mixed feelings about this, I was excited as I had never been before, but apprehensive of the outcome if my mum found him there with the so called other woman. When we got in the cinema the film had already started, my mum was leading, and I was closely following as I was struggling to focus in the strange gloom. She led me to some aisle seats and sat down. "There, look, look it's Jerry with his girlfriend," she whispered, and sure enough Jerry was sat at the side of us in the opposite aisle seat looking straight at us. As he saw us looking he turned to the girl at the side of him who lent forward to check us out.

Oh my this is awkward. I tried to focus on the film being shown but was well aware of the eyes burning into us from the opposite aisle. I could feel my mum trembling at the side of me from either temper or nerves. *How I wish this film would end so we could get out of here.* There was not a word exchanged between Jerry or my mum, just awkward glances but I refused to take my eyes off the screen. In different circumstances I would have enjoyed being here, seen it as a treat, but there was no way this was a treat – this was purgatory. Finally the film ended and the lights came on, I went to stand as to leave, but my mum pulled me back in my seat. "Wait," she hissed. Glancing over to Jerry and the mystery woman I heard Jerry sigh. As he rose from his seat holding the woman's hand she followed him down the aisle. I could not see her face properly her hair was jet-black, long with a centre parting that hung over her face like curtains obscuring her features. She appeared tall and was very slender her body appeared childlike. "Right come on we can go now," my mum announced, after this Jerry stayed away.

A few weeks later while I was at home with my mum, he walked in, slowly followed by the mystery woman. To say my mum looked shocked would have been an understatement. She stood and watched as they made their way into the sitting room, and stood in front of the open fire. Glancing at my mum for some kind of reassurance I could see she was at a total loss at what they were doing there. Jerry started to talk calmly, even kindly, addressing me. "Danielle, I am leaving and I won't be back. We are here because we want you to come with us, to come and live with us in our new home." My jaw dropped totally stunned, looking at my mum her mouth was also on the floor but her bottom lip was visibly shaking. "It's up to you, Danielle, you can go with them if you want," my mum managed to stammer. I could not believe I was even being asked this, asked this by the man who had physically and emotionally terrorised me for years. Why? Would he even want me? I knew my answer; it was a no brainer. My mum was far from perfect, but she wasn't the monster he was. "I'll stay here, I want to stay with my mum," I replied. Jerry actually looked upset by my response and turned to the woman he was with saying, "Well I tried, no one can say I never tried," and without a backward glance they both left.

25

A few days later on returning from school there was an open truck, typical to a scrap mans truck loaded up with all our belongings outside our house. My mum was stood talking to the driver and Ryan was also there. Unsure what was happening I approached them. "I have taken everything. I've not left him with a pot to piss in, Danielle. We are moving into a new house, and we will be living with Ryan from now on." I looked at the truck piled high with our belongings, strapped and clasped securely. "Come on, Danielle, where leaving right now, before he shows up." Grabbing my hand, my mum led me down the road.

"Are we not going in the truck, Mum?"

"No, Danielle, it's not far. Ryan and his mate will meet us there with the truck."

She was right, it was not far; in fact just a couple of streets away, and as we arrived the front door was open and Ryan and his mate were busy unloading the truck. The new house was on a busy main road. It was a typical terraced property two-up two-down with a kitchen at the back and a small back yard. When Ryan and his mate had finished unloading, to my mum's dismay Ryan announced he was off to the pub and would see her later. Which to be fair would have been OK except nothing had been put in its rightful place, which left me and my mum dragging beds, mattresses, wardrobes etc. up a flight of stairs. While we were busy mum told me that they had bought the property between them, and would have moved sooner but were waiting on all the legal stuff to be sorted before they got the keys.

The house was nice; it was warm and cheery, not like the old one that was damp and dreary. It had been nicely decorated and was in good order, with an open fire in the lounge and sitting room. My mum told me that Ryan was not working on the coal lorries anymore and had got a job working down the pit on the face. That's when I realised we had been moved by a coal lorry – how embarrassing. Well at least there was one, plus even though it was only a few streets away I was far away not to see Dawn and her mates.

I did not know Ryan. He had come round for his meals when doing his delivery at ours, but that stopped once I had dropped my mum in it. I figured he was obviously a drinker, and my mum was furious he had left us in such a pickle just to get a few pints. By the time he returned the place had started to take some order: we all had a bed to sleep in that was made up, the living room was straight and we were busy unloading boxes in the kitchen, hunting for the elusive kettle. My mum though obviously mad with him and for good reason, never said a harsh word to him when he came in, simply suggested a chip dinner.

Sooty had been shut up in my bedroom as furniture had been unloaded, and had been forgotten about in the hustle and bustle of getting straight. Ryan before going out to get the food, walked around to see what had been achieved while he was away. Opening my bedroom door Sooty shot out like he had the Devil after him, flying straight out the open front door Ryan had left open when he had returned. "Danielle," my mum screamed, "you were meant to be watching that cat. That's it you have lost him now, you stupid girl." Glaring up at her I really wanted to scream back at her and say, "well if your idle so-called boyfriend had done his job, instead of going to the pub then I would have been watching him, and not lugging up pieces of furniture five times and more my weight up a flight of stairs, so there." But obviously I didn't; I never answered my mum back, and anyway I could have been thrown out there and then, and then what would I have done, so as always I kept quiet.

That evening I was left alone in the new house, while my mum and Ryan went to the pub. I didn't mind too much, the place was nice and they had set up the television and had promised not to be too long. It was a school night, and I did not fancy going to bed without my mum being there and in a strange house. Thankfully they were back early as promised.

"Danielle, we have a surprise for you," my mum announced. Instantly I thought of Sooty. *Oh yes they've got my cat back.* "You are going to Italy with the school."

Italy? This was first I had ever heard of a school trip, nevermind all the way to Italy. "How come? I don't understand, Mum."

She went on to explain that in the final year of primary school, the school always does a holiday somewhere abroad for the children that are moving on to new schools, and this year it was ten days in Italy in the school summer holidays. Ryan and her had paid for me to go.

That night I slept well in the new house; it had not sunk in about me going away with the school, maybe I did not want to get my hopes up, in case I was disappointed and never got to actually go, so I put the whole idea of going away out of my head. As soon as school broke up my mum had me down town buying bikinis, shorts, tee shirts etc. you name it she was buying it. The only thing she didn't get was a suitcase as she said we already had one. She said it was big but she was sure I would manage. The night before going away mum dragged out the suitcase. To say it was big would be an understatement: it was as tall as me and bright green in colour. Laying it on the bed we placed in all my new holiday clothes. "Right Danielle, an early night for you, you're up early in the morning to catch the coach."

26

Two coaches were outside the school filled with excited youngsters, and there wereparents waving their children off. That morning my mum had given me some Italian spending money – the recommended amount suggested by the school. I was so excited I could not believe this was actually happening. There was no one on the coach I recognised so had sat in the first available seat I had come across, next to a small girl with freckles who had her hair tightly plated; it turned out her name was Jenny.

Jenny was quiet, which was a blessing as the teachers had us singing songs and gave us puzzle charts to keep us entertained. The teachers explained to us that we were travelling down to London, then catching a train and then the ferry at Dover, and then another train before finally arriving at out destination in Italy. All our mums had packed us a pack lunch for the start of our journey, which some of the children were tucking into before the coach had even left the end of the street.

Approximately two hours into our journey the coach in front of us broke down, giving our teachers palpitations as they were on a tight schedule. Luckily it was just a punctured tyre, which between both coach drivers they soon managed to repair. The journey was going swimmingly we had made up our lost time and was pulling into the London St Pancaras train station only to be sent away by a man in uniform, who announced the train drivers had gone on strike and there was only a few trains still operating.

Unsure if our train was still running, or of its departure time as the station was in total chaos and the teachers were getting no information. It was decided that a teacher would stay at the station and inform us as soon as they got any information on our train. The others decided we would do a short tour of London, so guided by them we visited St James park luckily we weren't there long before we were called back to the station to proceed our journey. This was the first time I had to move my suitcase, I had to carry it from the coach to the train, and then try and haul it onto the train itself with some effort I finally managed to drag it on.

The train pulled into our station and coaches were waiting for us, I managed to drag the case off the train and to the coach were the driver was putting everyone's cases in the storage space. My case was easily three times the size of everyone else's. "Looks like I'm going to need my muscles for this one. What you got in here. Your whole wardrobe?" he laughed. Blushing, I shook my head and quickly got on the coach.

The coach journey was boring and long, but finally the most wondrous sight I have ever seen came into view: The white cliffs of Dover. I had never seen anything as spectacular, or cliffs as big, in my whole life. I could not pull my eyes away from them. The coach pulled up and we all had to disembark and take our cases along a steep, narrow platform where, at the top, were customs asking for our passports. *Oh no this is it!* I had no passport, I was not going after all. Looking around anxiously at the other children and feeling like a thief that was going to get caught out at any minute. I sighed a sigh of relief as the teacher leading us pulled out a piece of paper, and unfolding it explained it was a multi passport covering everyone in our party. The passport controller quickly counted us all as we went through customs, then returned the paperwork back to our teacher.

We were told it would take roughly an hour to sail over to France on the ferry, and we were to get some lunch while we were waiting. Jenny and I found a food kiosk selling fast food and sat chatting tucking into our burger and chips. It was strange being on the ferry, even though we were in the middle of the English Channel going at I don't know how many knots, it did not feel like we were actually moving at all. The ferry soon docked in France and after collecting our luggage we made our way to the train station for the next leg of our journey.

We were informed we would be on the train all night, so to try and get some sleep we had been divided up and put into private carriages that fitted about eight of us. The teacher had flipped the seats up and given us a pillow and a blanket each to help us settle, but no one could sleep, we were all too excited. Every time they came to check on us we were laughing and giggling.

In the dark, through the windows I could make out what appeared to be snow-topped mountains. They looked huge and close enough to nearly reach out and touch. I must have drifted off as the next thing I knew a teacher's handing out breakfast of a lot of dry buns I had never seen before and a carton of juice, they're croissants one of the children announced, I didn't care what they were they tasted of dry cardboard give me weetabix any day.

The train pulled into a small station and we disembarked, luckily this time a teacher took my case. She sighed, probably thinking, *Who in their right mind would give a small kid a case this size*. The final train had already pulled into the station; it was an open carriage and we sat were we could among the other passengers. Not one of us made a sound on the train, we were all listening to the strange language that was filtering through the carriage. I was looking intently at these foreigners speaking in a different tongue, trying to pick up any words I recognised, or trying to figure out if their conversations were normal or if they were angry etc. But no, there was no telling and no recognition of any of their language. It all felt quite alien to me sat there with all this strange activity going on, looking at my fellow classmates I could tell they were as intrigued as me.

The train was full to bursting and pulling into its next station half a dozen more passengers squeezed on, hanging precariously from the straps attached to the trains ceiling.

They were being swung from left to right as the train continued its journey; they were getting quite loud, and in their foreign accent sounded angry and intimidating. It felt like at any moment they would lunge at us. I know it was probably nothing and just their strange accents, but I was relieved when we finally left the train and was on the final coach to our destination.

The coach pulled up outside a large hotel which was straight opposite the beach, we all rushed for the coach windows, trying to get our first glimpse of the sea. We were led into the foyer of the hotel, and split into groups of boys and girls and taken to our rooms. I was put in a room overlooking the beachfront. I was sharing with two other girls who had rushed in ahead of me, mainly because they weren't hampered with the case from hell, and had claimed their beds and were excitedly unpacking their cases. We exchanged names and were chatting about which outfit to wear first, when the teacher called us down for dinner. We were led into a large dining room and asked to choose between macaroni cheese or spaghetti Bolognese, being told that whatever we chose was our dinner for the whole holiday I wasn't too sure what macaroni cheese was so I chose spaghetti Bolognese.

After dinner there was a small meeting where the teacher explained the money to us and if we had the full amount what it broke down to each day as spending money. She explained we were on a half board basis which included our breakfast and evening meal each day, the trips we would be taking, one of which was a visit to a glass blowing factory. We were told we were allowed to explore the small area we were staying in but to go around as a group of two or more, and everyone had to be back for their evening meal so everyone was accounted for. It was so good to be in a proper bed that night, after sleeping on the hard train floor the night before. I could hear the boys in the room opposite play fighting and messing in their room but they did not disturb me for long; the lack of sleep, the heat and a comfy bed soon got the better of me.

27

We were woken by a tap on the door by our teacher the following morning announcing breakfast, we all quickly dressed, and made our way into the dining room. Our table was already set with our breakfast, it was the dry bread again, orange juice and either tea or coffee. I managed to eat it this time, as they had provided us with butter and a selection of jams and marmalades to sweeten the croissants and make them more palatable.

After the teacher announced it was a free day with no trips, so it would be nice if we all went on the beach for the day. There were no complaints as we all ran to change into our various swimwear. Stepping out of the hotel the heat hit you, and the sun's rays were blinding as it rebounded of the bleached white street. The beach was pure white, and the sea was glistening and looked so inviting with the suns heat and light reflecting from it. The girls I shared my room with had gone off to find their mates, but hearing a call of, "Come on, last one in is a ninny." I happily chased the others into the sea. The water surprised me, I expected to shudder and squeal like I would in the waters of Whitley Bay, but no the sea was warm and I could see the sand below, see my feet in the bottom of the clear water which fascinated me. I was soon up to my waist in the warm sea, swimming and laughing with the others. I spent everyday on the beach and swimming, I loved it – loved the freedom, loved the no restrictions, and loved just being a child, which the holiday allowed me to be.

I never spent much of my holiday money on myself, I never bought lunch, preferring to be on the beach, and just bought the occasional ice cream from the beach kiosk. So when we went on our trip to the glass blowing factory, I had the money to buy my mum a beautiful horse blown from glass. I stood and watched it being created from nothing more than a blob of glass. I was so chuffed with it, and the holiday she had given me, that I could not wait to give it to her on my return as I knew she would be thrilled with it too. What I was not so chuffed with was the hotel meals the same breakfast and dinner every single night. By the time the holiday was over, I was happy to get back, but the whole experience had been amazing and I would not have missed it for anything.

On arriving back to the school our parents were anxiously waiting. I could see my mum waving like crazy when she saw me through the coach window, and she was beaming from ear to ear. As soon as I got off the coach I was bombarded with a thousand questions by my mum: "You been OK?", "You enjoy it?", "How was the hotel?", "How was the weather?" and so on and so on. After reassuring her I was fine and had a great time and thanking them for the holiday. My mum told me they had been away, no where as fancy as me, but they had been away for a week to Mablethorpe. My mum appeared really happy, happier than I had ever seen her and content. Walking back home I held my mum's hand and Ryan took my other hand and they were swinging me between them, making me laugh as my feet swung through the air.

Arriving back home the house felt calm and safe, and I was not scared anymore. I finally knew Jerry was gone, and he would not be back to hurt me or my mum. Ryan, though I did not know him, was definitely a better bet than Jerry had ever been, and in the short time I had been with him he had never contradicted or threatened me either physically of verbally. Maybe finally things were going to start to look up, and the holidays were a new start for all of us.

28

No sooner was my case unpacked, than it was repacked for the journey up north to see my grandparents. My mum explained I would be only there a couple of weeks, as on my return we would need to sort my uniform for my new school. We took our usual journey to my grandparents' house, but when we arrived my grandad was in bed recovering from a heart attack he had suffered a few weeks earlier at work.

My grandma looked tired and worn, she said the doctor had put the cause of his heart attack down to a condition called angina, and he would be on medication for the rest of his life. Plus the chances were he would have more attacks as the attack had caused permanent damage to his heart. He needed quiet and as much rest as possible. I knew I was an inconvenience that my grandparents could do without, but as per-usual my mum was on the next coach out saying as my grandad was ill, two weeks was ample for my visit as if she was doing them a massive favour.

My aunties came every morning to walk Tanya, and take me out from under my grandma's feet. The strain on my grandma's face was obvious, she was trying to keep the house immaculate as she always did, plus take care of me and her sick husband. I would take drinks and food up to my grandad who was still bed bound; I would quietly tap on his bedroom door and wait for his weak response to enter the room. My grandma had propped him up on extra pillows, and I would sit talking to him while he slowly drank and ate his food. He looked awful, ashen, weak, but mainly vunerable. I would stay with him until my grandma called me away saying he needed to rest, if he was to make a full recovery.

By the time my mum returned to collect me, he had started to come downstairs in the day in his night clothes and a dressing gown as he had not the strength to dress himself. There was one thing he still managed to do, and it was in his words his only luxury, and that was that he enjoyed a smoke. My grandma would shake her head and frown at him as he slowly placed the cigarette paper in his tin, then added the tobacco, closed the tin; then as if like magic the cigarette would drop out. I had spent hours this holiday watching him roll his cigarettes, I so wanted to have a go, but I knew cigarettes were out of bounds, and I knew he would say no if I had asked. Plus I knew there was no way my grandma would have allowed me to have a go, even though I had no desire to smoke one.

My mum smoked like a chimney, she said they were the strongest on the market Park Drives and they stunk. Her fingers were discoloured with permanent tobacco stains, and no matter how much she scrubbed she could not remove them. Her clothes and hair reeked of stale cigarette smoke; she had purchased a cigarette holder to stop anymore damage to her fingers. It was long and thin and she would sit there smoking a cigarette with the holder majesticaly held in her fingers looking like a hollywood star, all glamourous on the local advertising billboards.

I was sad to leave my grandparents, but mainly my grandad, as I was not sure if I would get to see him again. Maybe he would die before my next visit. It wasn't fair, why could we not live nearer so I could visit whenever I liked? My mum was also worried about my grandad. Though she never said but I could tell by her eyes, and by the constant whispering between her and my grandma that she was concerned and upset. She was closer to her dad than her mum, she always said my grandma was a nag, and was constantly bullying my grandad who wouldn't stick up for himself, so my grandma treated him like a doormat. She blamed my grandma for his heart attack saying all the stress had caused it, plus she would never allow him out, if just even for the odd pint with his work mates to unwind after work.

My mum had a telephone connected on our return, so she could keep in touch with how they were both keeping. Apparently he was going back to work in the next couple of weeks. My mum felt he was not ready for that and blamed my grandma for forcing him back to soon saying, "She won't be happy until she has killed him, for christ sake. Can't she leave the poor man alone!"

I had turned eleven while at my grandparents', but this time there had been no fuss. I wasn't disappointed I understood my grandad was the main priority and if he got well that would be the only gift I needed.

It was two weeks before I started the local secondary school, so my mum took me to the schoolwear shop apparently each school had its own uniform, tie, blazer and badge, and this was the only shop that stocked what I would need. Entering the shop it was small and stuffy; a small man came forward asking what school I would be attending. I told him I was going to Ravensdale School. He disappeared, soon returning loaded down with a huge pile of clothes. "Right she is going to need all these."

My mum's face was a picture. "Are you sure? Surely not all those."

He then did a complete run down. "At the very least, she will need two blouses, two skirts, tie, blazer, badge, shoes, long socks in grey, one physical education skirt, one physical education top, apron for cooking class, 1 physical education shorts for gym mat work and finally a large bag to put everything in, as she will be loaded down with school books and homework. Personally I would suggest a satchel as she is tiny and the weight will be better distributed, saving a bad back. These should all fit." I could see my mum trying to figure out how much all this attire was going to set her back. "We have a savings scheme, if that will help. I can put some of this away for you, and just pay for what you can today." My mum looked disgusted at the very idea he would suggest she was unable to pay, and got me trying on everything I needed. Once satisfied she begrudgingly paid.

"The cost of this uniform is ridiculous, you better take good care of it. Why can't you just go in normal clothes? It would be much easier, not to mention cheaper." My mum moaned and grumbled all the way home. "Right, Danielle, take those clothes upstairs and hang them up properly. God help you if I find them on your bedroom floor."

Hanging my new uniform up, it hit me, this was it, I was moving on to pastures new. The uniform smelt fresh and crisp, the school badge was a bright yellow raven's head, and the tie was a combination of bright yellow and green stripes. I took the uniform back off the hangers, and put it on – checking myself out in my mum's long bedroom mirror. I looked lost in it, it wasn't because it was to big, it was a comfortable fit allowing plenty of growing room – I just looked too small to be wearing something so grown up and smart. No matter how I felt I was going to the new school, hopefully everyone would be nice and there would be a few people I knew moving with me.

29

Even though I had been entertained and busy all the school holiday with the trip away to Italy, visiting my grandparents and getting suited and booted for my new school, I still had my mum's voice ringing in my ear as clear as the day she had said it, hanging over me like a cloud of doom: "You were born in a *mental hospital.*" The very idea of it made me cringe with revulsion, made me sick to not just my stomach, but to my soul, my entire being, and no matter what, I could not shake off this despair. I wished I could close my eyes and the whole wretched conversation would be extracted from my memory, but no it hung over me, my skeleton in the cupboard leaving me feeling worthless, isolated and alone.

After all who could I trust to share such a huge secret with? If it had shocked me to my inner core, it would no doubt disgust whoever I told, who would no doubt go on to tell others and this was a risk I was not prepared to take.

All this hurt and hate I turned on my dad: after all it was his fault he went off with the other woman with four kids, caused my mum to end up in that evil place, and through no fault of her own gave birth to me there and now some how I had to live with the consequences, and try to stay normal, sane and well balanced. It was at these blackest points I wished Dawn had hit me with the house brick she had launched at me, and I had been found bleeding and dead in the passage. At least then I wouldn't be constantly depressed and miserable, I would be at peace. So far my life had been far from peaceful; it just seemed to go from one drama to another. As far as I was concerned my life was a total fuck up.

So it was no surprise that I was apprehensive about the move to my new school. I also could not get my cat Sooty out of my head, had he made it back to our old address safely without getting run over? Is he all right? Or had he starved to death? I needed to go back there and see for myself, but that place, that house, held so many bad memories, I was not sure if I was brave enough to go back. What if Jerry was there? Could I face seeing him again? He could attack me again, and who would stop him? After all no one would know I was there, he could finally drown me in that filthy outside toilet. The idea sent quivers down my spine.

Though then again there was the guilt gnawing away at me, Sooty was a defenceless animal still only really a baby. Christ, what was I going to do? He could be at the old house right this second scared, alone, hungry, vulnerable, crying at the front door like he always did, or Jerry could have hurt him, even killed him, vented his rage on him for my mum's moonlight flit.

I was eleven years old I shouldn't have to deal with all this, I should be playing with dolls, skipping, hanging out with friends, and the only worry I should have is the move to a new school. Instead I had to rationalise, consider consequences and risk, analyse, hide my emotions, and be secretive. I felt so much older than my years, in fact I was maturing quickly not only on the outside but emotionally. Everything that had happened to me made me not allow myself to trust anyone, not allow anyone to get to close as to hurt me and then to simply walk out of my life like my dad had. No my barriers were firmly up and they were staying up, no matter what I was told, no matter who I lost from my life I was not going to allow it to affect or hurt me again.

After my first day at my new school I decided I was going back to the old house, the guilt was too much, I needed to find out what had happened to Sooty no matter how bad it was. By the time I reached the old house I was trembling like a leaf and was in a cold sweat, my mouth was dry and I felt I would pass out at any second, but I was doing this, I was not turning back. The very sight of the house made me sick to my stomach, but then it dawned on me the house was empty, there was a for sale sign outside. Oh my, the house looked bleak: the windows were filthy, the paint was peeling off the frames. I knew the place was bad but now in its empty state it was appalling.

Sooty was not in his rightful place meowing at the front

door so, glancing around to check no one was around, I made my way up the passage to the back garden. The back of the property was worse than the front, I could hardly believe I had actually ever lived here, there was still no sign of the cat. *Oh no*, My heart sunk, he was gone. There was one last thing I could try. Going to the top of the garden I did the whistle he was accustomed to, and there in a flash Sooty came running up from next door's garden. I had never been so relieved to see anything in my entire life. With tears rolling down my cheeks I sat on the grass and Sooty was purring and rubbing into me. He felt so good, and he looked well considering he had been left all these months. All the while I was fussing him I was anxious and scared I would get caught, so now what was I going to do? Leave him here? Take him home? Hope the new owners would take pity on him, and take him in? I knew I had to do something, but what? Even though I was scared I stayed a long while fussing him and rocking him with tears streaming down my face. I loved this cat, I never wanted him, and now I didn't want to be without him.

Jumping free of my arms, Sooty suddenly shot off back into the neighbour's garden, peering over the fence I just managed to see that someone had returned home and he was purring round their feet. "You here again, puss. Come on then let's get you fed and settled." Oh thank god, the neighbours had taken him in, I had never ever seen the neighbours when I lived here but I was thankful for them now. It brought a lump to my throat to see Sooty being affectionate with a stranger, but then again what was he meant to do, he was such a lovely, affectionate cat that I was pleased he had found a good home and appeared safe, after all that's all I could wish for.

If I took him back with me what was to stop him getting out? And this time getting run over. After all the traffic was constantly busy. My mum might be mad at me for fetching him back, after all she had not mentioned about going and getting him. In fact she had never mentioned him since the move; it was as if in her eyes he had never existed. Ryan may also be cruel to him as Jerry had been. I had to be selfless and walk away. Another thing I had lost. I had made a pledge not to get hurt again, yet here I was sobbing like a baby over a dumb cat.

30

I kept quiet about my visit to the old house, like I had learned to keep quiet about everything. My mum still had no time for me, her life revolved around her work but at least now she had a nine-to-five job. Friday night, Saturday afternoon, Saturday night and Sunday afternoon they were at the local pubs from opening till close. They would always come back in a right state, and I would never know if they would come in giggling or arguing.

On one of their drinking sessions my mum arrived home early, without Ryan, saying she had come back to make dinner, and he would be following her back in around an hour when the meal was ready. This all seemed very odd, as this had never happened before, but my mum set about doing the meal, gave me mine, and then started pacing, checking and rechecking the clock on the kitchen wall.

"He told me he would be an hour, it's now been over

two. Wait until he gets in." She was livid she was literally spitting her words out.

I sat there quietly, eating my food, watching her getting more and more irritated. There was the sound of a key turning in the lock and no sooner had Ryan entered the room than she was at him. "So what was the idea of sending me ahead, to cook you a meal you had no intention of coming back for. What am I, some kind of mug? Or were you up to something? Up to no good no doubt? Well we can both play at that game, I've done it before and I can do it again. You see this dinner? I have a good mind to sling it in the bin, you son of a bitch." She was screaming at the top of her voice.

Ryan who had stood there totally shell-shocked by her outburst, finally flipped. Picking up the hot plate of food he said, "Laura, you can stick your food." The plate flew through the air and I watched it as it came hurtling towards me. I instinctively ducked at the table so it would not hit me, but luckily he had thrown it too high to get me. There was an almighty scream. Spinning round in my seat, the scream had come from my mum who had been stood behind me while yelling at Ryan. The plate had hit her full force in the face, and she was screaming hysterically with red-hot potato dripping from her left eye, Ryan fled, obviously appalled by his actions, without a backward glance or an apology.

My mum once she had composed herself, managed to call a taxi and we went to accident and emergency at the local hospital. On the way she made up this elaborate story and said I needed to stick to it and not to mention the real reason for her injuries. I figured she was mad, after all why would you cover up something like that. It was obvious the staff in the hospital did not believe a single word either, and just frowned at her as she explained how a bake potato exploded as she got it out the oven. Thankfully I was never asked what really happened; I was loyal to my mum, but in this instance I felt she was wrong so I would have probably told the truth.

We spent a few hours in there. Firstly they had to clean out the remains of any food lodged in her eye, then treat the burns and finally check for any permanent damage. When she came out she said it had been horrific, that they had to take her eyeball out and rest it on her cheek while they cleaned her up and checked the tissues etc. I knew she was exaggerating, as surely eyeballs can not be removed this way. Yet she had not given Ryan away for the assault. She said as far as they could tell there was no permanent damage, but obviously time would tell if it would affect her vision or not. Her eye was bandaged and they had given her drops to put in to stop her eye drying out and to help with her recovery.

Ryan was in when we got back, more concerned with if anything had been said than how my mum was and if the police would be a knocking. My mum reassured him all was well, and she had not dropped him in it. As it was Saturday night they both went back out to the pub my mum bandaged up and acting as if she didn't have a care in the world.

I as per-usual was left at home, trying to figure out

this bizarre catalogue of events. Why would anyone not say something to the hospital, police, friends? It made no sense. He may have done her permanent harm and yet she was keeping quiet, why? Has he some hold over her? Did she just love him unconditionally? Or was she scared to be alone? To lose her security and the stability of their relationship? Whatever it was I figured she was simply crazy, and to want me to cover up something as bad as that saying it was an exploding jacket potato, no way. If anyone asked I would tell the truth. I may have had to cover up a lot of my own abuse but I was not prepared to do the same for my mother.

The eye incident was not mentioned again, my mum thankfully had no lasting damage to her sight and the burns were only superficial. The only reminder she had of that day was that her eyelashes on her left eye did not grow out anymore, they grew in, causing her pain and having to go to the opticians to have them removed so they weren't stabbing her in the eye.

31

Ryan was loving working at the pit, and as part of his wage he got free coal delivered every month, more than enough to heat the house and sell some on the side. So my mum was apprehensive when he told her he had to give up his fuel allowance as everyone in the town had letters telling them it was becoming a smokeless area. The workers where Ryan worked had all received letters letting them know their employer was aware of the situation, and were offering to buy their coal allowance off them, and also give them loans to have the gas supply and all necessary work carried out.

So not really having any choice in the situation, Ryan got a pay out for his coal allowance and set up the loan with his employer. They decided they were having all the old fires ripped out and a gas boiler fitted in the cupboard under the stairs. A team of workmen arrived and the house was in total disarray as sledge hammers were smashing out the old fireplaces, floorboards were up everywhere as they laid pipes for the radiators. There was dust and debris everywhere.

The team of workmen were led by Max, a young man in his early twenties. Oh my was he fit, in fact he was the first male to ever draw my attention. He was a perfect match for David Essex. Long black wavy hair, immaculate even after his long shift in the house. He had dark brown eyes and a smile to die for that showed off his perfect white smile. When I got in from school he would always get me to put the kettle on and we would chat – well mainly he would chat, and I would stand there mainly gawking like a love-sick puppy.

I was gutted when the work was finished, which meant I would not see him again. He had showed us all how to operate the new system and said if there were any problems to ring him and he would try and sort it asap. The new heating worked perfectly. For the first time we had heat throughout the house; it was lovely waking up in the morning, whipping back the bed covers and still feeling nice and warm instead of dithering and having to quickly put on a dressing gown that had gone cold and damp in the night.

The school boiler had broken at school and we had been sent home early, so imagine my surprise to walk into the house and hear a lot of faffing coming from upstairs. I heard a man's voice: "Shit, who's that." Max and my mum nearly fell onto the landing in their rush to discover who had entered. Max's hair was all deshreveled and he was flushed, hastily zipping up his trousers; my mum was stood behind him trying to adjust her blouse. "Danielle, what the hell are you doing here?" my mum finally managed to stutter. Max decided to take control of the situation: "Hi chick, I'm just sorting out a prob with the rads up here." He threw me one of his huge Essex smiles and I felt my heart skip. It was more than obvious he was lying and it didn't help my mum standing behind him looking like the cat that had got the cream.

I did not move from the bottom of the stairs, I could not believe what I was witnessing. "Well I think you will find that's sorted now, so I will bid you both farewell." As he slowly came down the stairs I couldn't keep my eyes off him. Really, he had been with my mum, why? She was way to old for him. He was gorgeous, he could have any woman he wanted – any young, attractive woman he wanted, and yet here he was caught red-handed with my mum who was not ugly but she was just average. Had my mum come on to him? Possibly, as I could not see it being the other way round, but whatever happened it had obviously been mutual. Had my mum got him round here saying there was a fault, and then just jumped on him? Who knows, and obviously it wasn't something I was going to discuss with her. So it was just another secret to add to the rest I guess.

After Max left, my mum came downstairs, still flushed but acting as if all was normal. "What was wrong with the heating, mum?"

It was obvious she was flustered by my question. "Oh it was nothing, Danielle, just one of the radiators wasn't heating properly. He as sorted it now, so he won't need to come back." It was blatantly obvious she was lying and she knew I knew, but then again what was she going to say? "It's OK, Danielle, I just shagged the plumber, please don't give me away to Ryan." I had no intention of giving her away; things were far from perfect, but it was one hell of a step up from where we had been before. And if I did then what? We would be homeless because I couldn't keep my mouth shut. So no I was not saying a word, but to be honest I was slightly jealous. I had no experience with boys, after all I was only eleven, but my oh my was he fit. No wonder my mum was acting so smug.

32

My mum's drinking was escalating as well as their Friday night and weekend sessions. My mum had started drinking every night after work while Ryan was at work. I would never know what mood she would be in, as she slowly drank herself into oblivion every night. On good nights she would simply stagger to bed, but on others she would be evil, calling me names from a pig to a dog. It got to the point I was too scared to simply talk to her, as she would jump down my throat, making me feel worthless and ugly.

As Ryan worked shifts, on his days off he took an active role in the house while my mum was at work.

"Danielle, come and look at this, you'll never believe it."

Following him into the kitchen I saw he had dragged the twin tub into the middle of the room. "Open the lid, Danielle, I'm telling you I could not believe it. Your mums got a serious problem" I did as requested and peered in the twin tub. Both sides of the twin tub were full of empty bottles: wine bottles, sherry bottles, and barley wine bottles.

"Your mum's got a serious problem, something needs to be done. Only an alcoholic would behave like this." I stared at the bottles unsure of what to say. I was not shocked at what I was seeing, as I knew her drinking was out of control, just surprised she had been stashing all her empties there. Why not just put them in the bin?

"Someone needs to talk to her about this, Danielle." He was looking at me as if to say "Come on, volunteer, talk to her." I had not been able to speak to her for months without getting my head bitten off, so there was no way I was going to approach this subject with her.

"What am I meant to do with all these, for Christ sake? There's too many to bin." Looking exasperated he shut the lid on the twin tub and pushed it back into its rightful place. "Stuff her, she can sort the bloody washing – that's if she is in any fit state, that is." I took it from his actions he was not going to mention his find, or was going to wait for an appropriate time to bring up the subject, but he also knew my mums temper so I figured he was simply going to leave it.

Her drinking continued every night and every weekend like clockwork, she would come home in such a state she was unable to stand and I would be left to undress her and help her into bed. She was not light to move, and it would take all my strength to help her indoors and up the stairs to bed. My school work was suffering as I was not getting any proper sleep, and if I was in bed whether in the week or at weekend I would get hauled out of bed to assist my mum in one way or another. Ryan still went out with her every weekend. Saturday mornings were the worst as they would both get so drunk on the Friday night they would spend all Saturday morning arguing only to get ready a few hours later to do it all over again.

I had school friends but never invited anyone round; I was too ashamed. It would either be a case of my mum sat slowly drinking herself to oblivion, or ranting and screaming like a maniac making a right show of me. I went to my friends' homes occasionally. I would be welcomed by a smiling mother and a warm and cheery home. I enjoyed these visits but they were rare as I felt I could never invite anyone back.

The one thing I did enjoy was swimming. My mum had actively encouraged me to do well at swimming at school as she was petrified of the water. So every Sunday morning I went and let of some steam at the local baths. I used to get a coloured wristband that told the attendance when your hour was up. I loved it and I used to do lap after lap after lap. The only strokes I was any good at were front crawl and backstroke; by the time my hour was up I must have done at least fifty laps, but it revived me and gave me a little me time.

While at school one day they called me in to see the school nurse. "Hi Danielle, this is just a routine check up. I am simply going to take your weight and height." Taking off my shoes I stood under the scale as she lowered down the marker. "144 cm yes, that's fine, now your weight, Danielle. Hop on the scales." I watched as the scales finally settled on 3 and a half stone. "OK Danielle, thank you, you can put your shoes back on now," I watched as she busied herself writing down her figures. I was no expert but 3 and a half stone, surely that was never right for an eleven year old girl? "Right, Danielle, I am a little concerned about your weight. It's probably nothing to worry about, but to be on the safe side I will send your mum a letter to get you checked out by your doctor."

The letter arrived the following week, and my mum had me straight to the doctors.

"Hello Mrs Jackson, what can I do for you today." My mum explained the school's concerns. "Is she eating OK? Got plenty of energy?"

My mum glanced over at me with the look that all parents have. "She is fine, she eats like a horse," my mum reassured him.

"Then you have nothing to worry about, Mrs Jackson. Some children are just slower developers, as long as she is eating and full of beans, there is nothing to concern yourself about."

I felt alright, never really hungry, so maybe the stress was affecting my weight. Constantly having to play on my wits and living on my nerves was affecting not just my mental state but also my physical well being. Over the next few years my situation never altered: my mother continued to drink, the weekly arguments continued and I was left to pick up the pieces. I grew tall and lanky and virtually a nervous wreck, scared of my own shadow and too scared to stick up for myself as I was always put back in my place by my mother's sharp, cutting and spiteful tongue.

33

My grandma raised her concerns when I went on my yearly visit. "Laura, how come she is so skinny? And she doesn't seem right. What's going on with her?"

My mum would make up excuses, saying I was having problems at school, that I did not like it. My grandma offered to take me in to live with her, if it would make things easier, but my mum refused point blank saying no matter what I was staying with her. My grandparents weren't pleased but they had to accept her decision regardless.

My mum had warned me that I was not allowed to tell them about Ryan, that as far as they were concerned she was single and managing by herself, but I told my aunties on one of our morning walks out with Tanya as I felt I could trust them. They had been quizzing me on how we were getting on by ourselves, and how I must have been relieved to see the back of Jerry and all the endless arguments. That's when I let it slip we weren't on our own, we were living with Ryan. I was reprimanded there and then, and told not to tell lies and that they thought I was better than that. That was the first time I had reached out to anyone about my circumstances, but I was left feeling flat and wretched. It was obvious I had nowhere to turn – my mum had covered all the angles and who was going to believe me I was just a kid.

My mum had become friendly with the neighbours who had a Patterdale dog called Ella. They went out together, occasionally socialising at the local pub. My mum, all excited, announced Ella was having pups and she was getting one. The neighbour Kelly worshipped Ella and treated her like an extra child, and was as chuffed as anything she was having pups. My mum was counting down the days until she got her new dog. She decided on a male dog and called him Whisky. Just like Kelly she doted on him, taking him everywhere with her. On our annual holiday he was sent to the local kennel that had been recommended by a friend. On our return my mum insisted that I went and collected him while she unpacked. I didn't want to fetch him as I had been with her when he was dropped off and I remembered the huge sign on the gate: 'NO VISITORS WITHOUT MAKING A PRIOR APPOINTMENT, THESE PREMISES ARE PATROLLED AT ALL TIMES BY SECURITY DOGS, RUNNING FREE'. Plus I had seen the dogs patrolling the perimeter when we dropped Whisky off: two great evil-looking Doberman. I reminded my mum of all this but she shrugged it off. "Don't be daft, Danielle, they know you are going for him – I have rang them."

Still feeling apprehensive I set off. It was a long walk to the kennel, and all the way there I was cursing my mum for having to fetch him. The kennel was set in its own grounds, with no other properties around, as I walked up the lane towards it, there as I had remembered was the warning to keep out. *Bloody hell, what was I doing? this was madness.* There was no sign of the Doberman but I was sweating as I lifted the latch on the gate. As the heavy wooden gate was pushed open it gave out a loud screech from the hinges, my heart jumped into my mouth as I slammed the gate shut again still expecting the maneaters to fly out at me, but no, there was nothing. Relieved I realised my mum must have called ahead and, reopening the gate, walked towards the office block to request Whisky back.

As I approached the building an Alsation that was laid casually up against the office flew at me. I began screaming in sheer panic, fearing for my life. The Alsation raised to its full height and pinned me up against the wall, snarling and growling. I closed my eyes as I saw its jaws coming closer and closer to my face. It locked its teeth onto my left ear and I knew at any second he was going to tear my ear off.

"Christ, NO. Dollar, get down, get down this instant." Opening my eyes I saw a middle-aged couple running across the yard. "Dollar, leave, leave this instance." The Alsation immediately did as instructed, thankfully leaving my ear intact and ran up to its owners. I slid down the wall into a grovelling heap. The woman looked horrified. "What are you doing here?" she asked, I could not speak, taking my hands they led me into the office.

"Geoff, go and get her a strong drink of tea with

plenty of sugar and I'll try and find out why she is here."
I didn't want a drink but she forced it on me. "So why are
you here? Did you not see the sign?" Of course I had, I
wasn't stupid, but my mother had got me in this mess, I
could have been mauled to death.

I explained I had come to get Whisky and that my
mum had rung ahead they exchanged puzzled looks. "I
had no phone call, did you?" she asked Geoff. Geoff
shook his head; it was obvious she had not rung.

"Are you going to be alright getting back, do you want
us to call anyone to get you?" She was genuinely concerned,
the Alsation Dollar had gone back to laying in the sun and
had lost complete interest in me, and looked like butter
wouldn't melt. Reassuring her I was alright I collected
Whisky. On my return my mum asked if it had gone alright
I told her the full story but she was still insistant she had
phoned ahead.

Ryan and my mum were both doing well in their jobs
and decided it was time to move up the property ladder,
they finally settled on a small two-bedroomed bungalow
in Forest Town on a modern estate. My granddad was still
having problems with his heart and had suffered another
few attacks, the final one had been fatal and taking him in
the night. My poor grandma had found him dead at the
side of her the following morning and was devastated.
My mum and I went to his funeral. It was only a small
gathering just family and a few work mates. I sat in the
funeral car looking at the hearse as it made its way slowly
to the crematorium, my mum silently sobbing at the
side of me. I felt empty, I wanted to cry and could not

understand why I was unable too. I loved my granddad but my emotions were dead, I just could not connect to them. I felt guilty for not crying, for not being able to comfort my grandma or ease her pain.

My mum's sister and her husband had an extension built on the side of their home, which was converted into a living room for my grandma to live in.

My mum was furious, "I can't believe that she has sold her home, and given them the money to build that extension. They're not bothered about her, they're more interested in adding value to their own home. What about me, what do I get?" She hated her elder sister, believing she was favoured over her. I understood why my grandma had made the decision to move in with her daughter and husband. My grandparents had owned their house since they had been married, all the memories and history wrapped up in that house would have been to much to bear on her own. Once my grandma moved, my visits to stay with her each summer stopped. As my mum and her sister despised each other we were not welcome at her house, not even for a quick visit.

34

My mum continued drinking alcohol every night and she had discovered a cheaper way of doing this as the local public house would fill her empty bottle up for her with sherry, and when she ran out she would send me out to get her refills at all hours of the night. It was a good half an hour walk to the pub from where we lived. I was petrified but no amount of protesting worked. At nine or ten o'clock I was sent out petrified as it was 1978 and during the reign of the Yorkshire Ripper.

The papers and news were full of stories about him, how he was alluding the police, and who was his latest victim, and here I was at fifteen being forced to get my overbearing mother her fix and too scared of her to refuse. Every passing car or shadow made me jump, I could hear my heart beating like a drum in my chest. Christ, I hated her. As I entered the pub the barmaid scowled at me as I asked for her refill, not even questioning my age or what

I thought I was playing at, but at least being in there was sanctuary before having to go back out into the cold and dark.

Her relationship with Ryan had hit an all time low, they were constantly arguing, and when they had been out for their weekend drinking sessions it always ended in violence with Ryan lashing out at my mum because she was constantly nagging him. She would go on and on at him for hours. I would watch him, he would not answer her back, she was way too intelligent and he could never win an argument. He would sit picking at his nails until they bled, clenching and unclenching his fists until he would snap and lash out at her to stop.

My grandma came to visit when I was eighteen. She told me my mum had told her everything about Ryan and me, that he had an unnatural attraction towards me and I needed to leave as what we were up to was wrong. As far as I was concerned Ryan was nothing but my mum's boyfriend, we had a laugh together, would play cards occasionally, watch a bit of wrestling, and that was it, so I forgot about my grandma's warning.

As I was eighteen I was working in a local store in town, and had a steady boyfriend, John, that I had been seeing since I was sixteen. It was a long-distance relationship as he lived in Derbyshire and I lived in Forest Town. Not too far I admit, but as neither of us drove we only saw each other on a Friday night. He would come over to mine on a Friday evening.

He was never made welcome. My mum and Ryan

made it obvious he was an inconvenience, even resorting to switching off the lights and television, announcing they paid the bills and to get out of their house. We used to retreat to the local pub until he caught the last bus home. John unsurprisingly got sick of this set up, and tried to convince me to move in with him and get a house in Derbyshire, but I knew it wouldn't work and I was scared to get to close to someone and be let down yet again.

My next boyfriend my mum loved. I had not been interested in him, he had simply given me a lift home, but the next day he turned up on the doorstep a bottle of wine in each hand. It turned out he made his own wine and had bottles and bottles of it. "Barry, you can come over anytime, Danielle's always home by five." So there I was sat on the settee with a guy I had no interest in, my mum smiling like a Cheshire cat and making small talk as long as he kept bringing her the wine.

"Danielle, have you thought about getting your own place?"

"No, Mum, why?" She peered over at me from under her wine glass. "Well to be honest it's time you left." Ryan was sat watching the television but looked up. "I know what's going on with you two. You are nothing but a cheap tart, sleeping with your own mum's boyfriend. Disgusting, disgusting that's what you are."

Ryan jumped to his feet. "What the hell are you on about, woman? Are you mad?"

Raising to her feet, staggering with the effects of the wine, she began hollering at the top of her voice. "Don't treat me like a fool, I know, I know evvverything, and I want her out, I want her gone. I can't stand to even look at her. Get out of my sight before I kill you." Lunging towards me, I managed to dodge her. Completely mortified by what I had heard, by her sick allegations, I grabbed my coat and fled into the night with no idea where I was going or what I was going to do next.

35

Rushing out of the house I could hear my mother raging after me. "You bitch, don't you dare darken my door again," as if I ever would after her sickening accusations. It turned my stomach. Ryan was to me an old man, fat and repulsive. I had never thought of him as anything but my mum's boyfriend.

My mind was working ten to the dozen as I walked through the darkness, going over how she had spoke to me, and the things she had said. How could she even think that and where had it come from? Again I couldn't get it out my mind how much I hated her, and that this was it, I was never going back. I was not focusing at all on where I was going, it was as if my legs had taken over my body and were taking me on some kind of mystery journey. Looking down at my feet they were moving at the speed of light as if I was travelling on an airport travelator.

"Owch." I was flung back, my head was spinning, in my haste not looking where I was headed I had made full contact with a street light pillar. I reached up and felt my head looking at my hand half expecting blood to be there, but no all I had achieved was a nasty lump the size of an egg.

Cursing myself for my stupidity, I looked around, I had covered a good few miles and was half way between what was my home and town. I stood there, lost. Where was I meant to be going, I had no real friends apart from work colleagues and I had no idea where any of them lived. Plus if I did, would I be brave enough to just turn up on their doorstep having to explain what had happened? No that wasn't an option. Sitting on a low wall I tipped out my handbag. I had no idea what was in there but out came a million and one receipts, an old strip of spearmint, a pack of hankies, my house keys and lastly my purse. Sighing thankfully for small mercies, I tipped it out: one pound seventy five pence. Damn, I was in a proper mess.

I felt the tears stinging my eyes, what was I going to do. I had nowhere to go. I decided to keep heading down town. As I got closer I could hear the late revellers shouting and music coming from the local pubs. I was not dressed for town I was still wearing my work clothes. Damn, work. I had forgotten all about that; I had to be there at nine the next day. I had no idea what time it was and I could not afford not to turn into work. Losing my job on top of everything else was the last thing I needed right now, and my manager would be livid. Damn what a mess.

Right now, I needed somewhere safe to get my head

down for the night. At least it wasn't raining and it was relatively mild for the time of year. I could hear the squeals and laughter of a couple walking towards me. For some illogical reason I felt fearful and like I needed to escape, hide. I could not face anyone right now. I don't know if it was the fear of strangers approaching or the fact I loathed myself to the pit of my stomach for the fact that my mum would think I would betray her with her boyfriend, and it was as if anyone who saw me would know, know what I was, or being portrayed to be, and instantly judge me unfairly for it.

Looking blindly around for an escape like a rabbit caught in the headlights, I could feel my heart racing as if it was going to burst; my palms were clammy and I was sweating uncontrollably. I needed to get away. Turning back around and retracing my steps, this time looking around for any plausible bolt hole, across the road there appeared in the dark to be two large gates. I recognised the place immediately: Carr Bank Park. Running across the road not even checking for any oncoming traffic. The couple appeared to be getting closer and I was feeling physically sick to the point of wretching, running through the park gates I was brought to an instant stand still as the darkness hit me. It was totally black, pitch black, there was not a single light to light my way. I could hear the footsteps of the strangers approaching, even the conversation they were having was within ear shot. I had no choice, I had to walk deeper into the dark. Taking a deep breath I steeled myself to go on, every step was terrifying as I could not see an inch in front of my face, so, walking blindly with my arms outstretched, I took tentative steps. I had been to the park in the past as a child in the daylight, and now was trying to envisage it as I stepped forward, it had been years ago though.

There was not a sound, not even a bird tweeting or the tree leaves rustling to guide me on my way, just the sheer darkness like a wall of black. I considered turning back I glanced behind but the steps I had taken were gone and it was as dark behind me now as in front. Hesitating, unsure where to turn, or what to do for the best, I tripped, flying forward, landing face down in the dirt. Feeling stupid and embarrassed more than hurt, I pulled myself to my feet. Edging my foot forward I felt something solid in front of me. Reaching out I touched something cold and narrow – what was it? Following the line of the rail I realised where I was: I was walking in a kind of circle it was the park's bandstand. Continuing round I finally came to the entrance. I vaguely remembered how the bandstand looked in daylight, I knew it had a roof, was made of metal, and was roughly at the centre of the park. Slowly walking onto the bandstand I walked around this time on the inside, touching the sides as I went. I felt safe as I realised the bandstand was totally enclosed by metal on all sides apart from the entrance. From what I could feel it felt like a typical bandstand with open metalwork making up the structure but even though I was still enveloped by the dark it felt safer being enclosed in the smaller space of the bandstand. Knowing there was nowhere else to go, or anyone to turn to, I settled myself down for the night. The floor was cold and felt damp, so I removed my coat and used it as a groundsheet to protect me from the cold floor. Golly, this was going to be one long night. The silence of the park no longer unnerved me; it felt calming and safe. Not knowing what to do or how to comfort myself in such a bizzare situation, I started humming softly to pass the time away.

I must have drifted off, as a light suddenly startled me awake. It took a few seconds to take in what was happening and where I was, but there was definitely a light moving backwards and forwards as if it was being swung back and forth. Christ. I couldn't let anyone see me like this, how humiliating. I shuffled back and curled myself into the tiniest ball humanly possible. There was also singing; whoever had the torch was singing to themselves as they walked through the park. I peeped out and could see the torch being swung back and forth lighting their way, who ever it was had not seen me, they were more focused on getting through the park and home judging by the speed they were going. The light from their torch suddenly hit the front of a building, it was impossible to make it out from the dim light of the torch but there was definitely a building a few yards from where I was hiding. Could someone possibly live there, own a house in the middle of a park? Surely not. I was intrigued, and wanted to investigate but then again I didn't want to be seen by who ever possibly owned it.

Deciding it was best to stay put, I settled back down and eventually managed to go back to sleep.

Yuk, what was that brushing against my face. Something

had just walked or crawled across my face, itching my face where the perpetrator had been. I slowly opened my eyes and I was immediately to my feet: there were at least three rats scuttling across the floor as shocked to see me as I was to be disturbed by them. No way can this night get any worse. The night was fading and the outline of the building opposite was now visible. It shone like a beacon as if saying, "Come here I will keep you safe".

Thankfully there was no one about as it was still too early so, I tentatively made my way up to the building in front of me. Drawing closer it emerged as a magnificent property, grand in style and appeared old as if it carried a lot of history within its walls. The front door was set back within its structure with a step up to the door. Sitting on the step I surveyed my surroundings. The sun was coming up and the park and grounds looked amazing, a few birds were now showing themselves and the early morning haze was rising from the damp grass. I had no idea what time it was. I was tired, so tired I was using the door as a back rest and I soundly dropped back to sleep.

"What are you doing here? Are you OK?" Blinking up from my sleep, I could see there was a woman stood there in her thirties, well dressed. Damn this must be the owner.

"Sorry I didn't mean any harm. I'll be on my way."

Pulling myself to my feet I was stiff and aching. "Are you sure you're OK? Have you been out here all night? You must be freezing." Her sympathy was the last thing I needed. I didn't want to explain myself to anyone.

"I'm OK, what time is it?"

Looking concerned, she glanced down at her watch. "It's twenty to nine."

Oh no I was going to be late for work. The woman was blocking my exit, and I had to barge through her. "Sorry I have to go."

She was shouting after me, "No please wait, I maybe able to help you. Please come back and see me, you're too young to be out on the streets."

Her words stung me. Here was this total stranger who had never set eyes on me more concerned about me than my own mother had ever been. She was probably in bed sleeping off the effects of last night's drinking session oblivious of her actions. For now I had to get to work, but I was a mess, I needed to clean up first. Walking into town I made my way to the public toilet. Looking in the mirror the image that stared back was disgusting. My mascara had run down my cheeks leaving a trail, there were black circles under my eyes that gave away my night's antics, and my hair looked like a bird's nest. Turning on the tap I grabbed as many sheets of toilet roll as I could hold put it under the tap and scrubbed my face to remove all the traces of the old makeup. I did look fresher, but my hair was a mess. Tipping out my bag into the sink, I frantically searched for a comb; no I was out of luck. There was a small piece of paper tattered and torn. Opening it I sighed a sigh of relief as I realised it was Ryan's dad's phone number. Maybe he would take me in. He was always moaning he was hard up, it could be worth a go.

Boots was my next port of call before work. Looked like I needed to spend some money on a comb if I was attending work today. The shop assistant tried to stay professional selling me the comb but it was obvious she was stifling a giggle. Going to the makeup section I looked in one of the mirrors and detangled my locks. Eyeing up the makeup, I noticed the samples and there was everything I needed: mascara, foundation, blusher, eye shadow and lipstick. I had not got time to pick and choose so I opted for all the neutral shades and admired myself in the shop mirror – actually, not too bad. Looks like I can pull this off.

I knew as soon as I stepped into the shop it would be "Danielle, what time do you call this? You'll have to work through your dinner," blarr blarr. Today though she seemed preoccupied with a customer who obviously knew more about her consumer rights than she did and was getting herself in a tiss. By passing them down the middle aisle of the shop to avoid being seen, I went in the back and hung up my belongings, picked up some stock and busied myself restocking some of the shelves.

"Oh, Danielle, there you are. Pleased to see you're keeping busy, once you have done that can you rearrange the items in the window." Not waiting for an answer she returned to her agitated customer who looked like they were about to burst a gasket.

At lunch time I called Ryan's dad. "Hi Chris it's Danielle. I was wondering if I could come and stay with you for a while?" He was surprised to hear from me but thankfully didn't pry and instantly agreed to my staying. At least that meant not another day on the street or the park.

I had nothing but the clothes I stood up in and so I needed some of my belongings. I had the keys to get in and if I did, I could get some fresh clothes, toiletries and my bank book, but right now I had nothing and no way of replacing anything. I needed a plan. My mum and Ryan would both be out until the evening working, but they both got back before me. There was only one thing for it I would have to fake a sicky and get away from work early; I needed to get in and out of there before either of them were back.

After lunch my manager was still vexed with the morning customer who got the better of her, so I needed an Oscar-winning performance to fool her.

"Michelle?"

"What? This better be good after the day I'm having."

OK the playing sick won't do it, I am going to have to up the antie.

"Sorry, Michelle, but my mum has just met me at lunch, and told me my dog's been run over and it's not looking good. He may need putting down." I started to blubber.

"Oh no, Danielle, that's awful." Sniffling I continued, "The vet reckons he won't make it until I finish work, and all I want is to say goodbye to him."

Putting her arm around me she said, "Danielle, you go. You are no use to me like this, and I will see you in the morning, if you are up to coming in that is." I muttered my thanks and rushed for my coat I hated lying to her, but what choice did I have?

Luckily as I arrived at the bus station my bus was in. Sighing a sigh of relief I boarded the bus. I just wanted to get in and out of the place as quickly as I could to avoid seeing them. The house was empty when I got there, and I had no intention on hanging about. Snatching the suitcase from under my bed I filled it with my personal belongings, and put my bank book in my bag. I did not know where I was going from here but this place did not feel like home it had not for a long time, what with their constant fights that on occasions escalated into violence on both sides. It was a relief to be going and I had no intention of returning ever. I decided as I was never seeing her again, to leave her a farewell letter telling her exactly what I thought of her.

To Mum,

It gives me great pleasure to tell you I am leaving and I won't be back. You are a poor excuse for a mother. Who in their right mind tells their daughter their father's dead when they're not. You have never been there for me and it's a relief that I never have to set eyes on you ever again. You are dead to me as far as I'm concerned.

Danielle

I placed the letter on the bed. Funny how it's come to this for me to finally tell her how I feel if only in a short note. I was always too timid, scared and to insecure to ever back chat her or tell her what I thought, but right now I could not give a damn, after all she had made it clear she did not give a damn about me, with her mad accusations and game playing.

I knew where Ryan's dad lived, it was not far away, on a local council estate, known as the Bellamy Road Estate.

When I arrived at Chris's house, I rang the bell and stood on the doorstep, unsure what kind of welcome I would receive. He immediately answered the door with a huge smile and beckoned me in. "Kettle's on, Danielle. Mine's tea with two sugars."

We sat and chatted and I explained how I would just stay until I sorted something more definite and would pay my way; after, he showed me my room, which was a pretty floral single bedroom. Left there with my own thoughts, I realised I had not eaten all day, yet was not hungry. I had absolutly no appetite, maybe it was due to the shock of the latest events. More than anything I was exhausted, I needed rest. Laying on the bed I tried to fight the sleep as it was still early.

36

Opening my eyes the room had gone dark. I laid there adjusting my eyes, it took me a few seconds to remember where I was, and what had happened within the last twenty four hours. It all came rushing back to me, the predicament I now found myself in, what was I going to do. There was no way I could stay here for long it was not fair on Chris, he hardly knew me. Apart from the odd visit to see Ryan and my mum he was never around and when he was we only passed pleasantries so basically I was living with a stranger.

I needed the toilet. The room was pitch black and I had no idea where the light switch was. I laid there until I couldn't bear it any longer. Slowly getting up I managed to manoeuvre around the room and flick on the light switch. On a bedside cabinet there was a small clock showing it was half past one. After relieving myself I went back to bed; the rest of the night was spent tossing and turning I was unable to settle even though I was shattered. Cursing myself I watched the clock tick off what felt like every second; eventually it hit seven, the time to get sorted for work.

Going downstairs Chris was already up. "Morning, Danielle, your breakfast is in the kitchen."

Smiling shyly I thanked him and ate the breakfast he had kindly made.

"Danielle, it's none of my business what's been going on, but if your determined not to return home, then we can go to the council to see where you stand on being given some emergency accomodation and the sooner you do it the better."

The thought of living on my own was daunting but there was no way I was going back to the way things were. Agreeing to his proposal I rang into work explaining I was still distraught over my pet.

Chris had rang ahead to the council and had managed to get me an appointment for that morning. The advisor was very understanding, unknown to me it turned out my mum had already put my name down for social housing as soon as I had turned sixteen, so they were able to offer me a one bedroom flat on the Bellamy Road Estate. Chris was brilliant and he helped me get it decorated, he was struggling financially himself so I gave him some money for helping me with the decorating.

The flat was in a block of four, two downstairs and two above; they were all identical: a door leading from the communal landing that then led into the flats corridor, a double bedroom to the left straight opposite was the bathroom small but adequate and clean, at the end of the corridor the flat opened up into a large living space with a small gallery kitchen at the end overlooking the car park. The view from the lounge window was stunning as it was overlooking fields as far as the eye could see and, being on the top floor the view was amazing especially first thing when the sun came up.

Luckily as I had not been one for socialising or spending extravagantly on myself: I had managed to save quite a healthy amount to furnish my new home. I had no idea of the cost of things, but looking at the two and a half thousand in my current account I figured I would be able to buy the necessities. Taking a pen and paper and looking around the empty flat I started a list. Carpets, cutlery, plates etc, pans, bed and bedding, sofa and chairs, curtains, cooker, washer, food, cleaning stuff, bath towels, tea-towels, telephone installed, television or radio. As I was writing I could feel my budget shrinking and feeling inadequate. Well there was no use feeling inadequate, I needed to get started.

Not knowledgable of the prices of anything I needed, I decided to start at the local second-hand furniture shop. The living room was vast and I was not planning on overfilling it, so as long as the suite was in reasonably good nick and clean I was happy. I finally settled on a grey draylon suite there was not a mark on it, and it seemed OK for the seventy-five pound they wanted for it, which also included delivery. The carpets though, there could be no skimping on them, so I arranged for a local tradesman to sort a price for the whole flat, and once they were laid I would be happy to move in and have everything else delivered once they were down.

Dropping off the pans, cutlery and other kitchen items I needed at the flat, there was a knock at the door.

"Hi I'm Jake, I live in the flat opposite. Sorry if I'm imposing it's just I know how hard it is to get set up, especially if it's your first time. So I wanted to let you know that the council are doing a flat clearance from the block next door and there is a double bed in there and there's not a mark on it. It's just been dumped on top of the skip. My mates here we will fetch it up if you want, but if you're not bothered I won't be offended, just thought it was a shame if you missed out."

Unsure whether to agree or not and not wanting to offend my new neighbour I agreed, hesitantly unsure what I had let myself in for. A bed out of a skip, really? Is this what I had come to?

Luckily the bed was as Jake had described; it was not new, but it looked clean and they kindly put it together and would only accept a cup of tea as payment, which gave me an excuse to use the new kettle though he had to provide the tea, sugar and milk. When they left I looked at my first piece of furniture. I was still unsure a bed out of a skip really. Maybe I was being silly, after all I had no idea the cost of a new one, and the trip round Woolworths had been an eye-opener. Who would have thought kitchen bits and pieces could cost so much, so maybe the bed was a blessing after all.

Finally after another two weeks the carpets were down, and the place was starting to look like a home, my home, my first real home. It was time to move in. I had got most of my items from second-hand shops where I could the washer, cooker and television making sure I got a guarantee of at least six months. Turning the key in the door I entered the flat, the smell of fresh paint still lingered in the air making it smell clean and it mingled with the freshness of the new carpets. I had to admit I had the place looking good, it was just a pity I had no one to show it off to. Oh well it was my home and it was safe. I finally had some control, shutting the door behind me I put my first lot of food shopping away, walked over to the lounge window and watched the sun go down over the fields. I felt at peace, safe. I could not remember the last time I felt so relaxed, no more rows, drunken arguments, no feeling everything was out of my control.

37

Life was good, I was loving living on my own. I loved coming home at night after work closing the door and being able to shut the whole world out. I had got a telephone installed, not that I had anyone to ring, or to ring me, but it was my safety net with living alone. You could never be to careful, or if I took ill, or needed to call work. The flat was still sparsley furnished and I had done it all within my budget and still had some to spare. The rent was fifty-six pound a month and included heating, so I could easily manage on my wage, and as I was by myself not tied to anyone. I was picking up extra shifts where needed just to pass my time.

Arriving home after a long shift Jake was waiting for me on the landing.

"I thought you would never get back, I have a message for you, from your mum." The mere mention of her name made my heart sink. Puzzled my mum, what the hell did she want? And how did she find me?

"She told me to tell you she needs to see you as your gran's not well. She will be in the Prince Charles pub tomorrow from one o'clock, and she wouldn't have bothered you but it's urgent."

Thanking him I made my excuses and let myself in my flat; suddenly the place didn't feel so safe. I really didn't need this, how on earth did she know where I was? I didn't want to see her, she was the last person I wanted to see, but it was my gran. Damn her, I had no choice – I would have to go.

Entering the Prince Charles pub there they were in their usual seats on a Sunday afternoon getting a skin full. Ryan was the first to spot me; he shuffled uncomfortably in his seat and nudged my mum, who looked up and gestured at me to join them. Standing in front of them as I had no intention of staying I just wanted the news on my gran and I was leaving.

"Danielle sit down, I can't talk to you while your towering above us and I don't want everyone else listening in." Sighing I pulled a chair up, she then continued. "Look if you are not interested in me and your family that's fair enough you just have to say."

Refusing to answer such a stupid statement I simply asked how my gran was.

"There's nothing wrong with her, I just said that as I knew it was the only way you would agree to see me."

Glaring at her I could not believe my ear.

"Look, Danielle, I have something to tell you, it's regarding your dad. He has been trying to track you down and if you want to see him he is waiting for you at the welfare just across the road.

181

It didn't know wether to laugh in her face or cry. "OK, Mum, let me get this straight. You have used my gran to get me here by making out she is virtually on her deathbed, to tell me my dad who has not given a damn about me, wants to see me across the road?" I was livid. How dare she sink so low. I needed to get out of there before I said or did something I would regret. My mum was speechless, I had never ever answered her back and the shock on her face was laughable. She reached out to touch my hand but I brushed her off and stood up with such force that it sent the chair tipping back I had been sitting on.

"Please, Danielle, go and see him." Ignoring her I left the pub.

She used my grandma to get me to come over, the bitch. How could she use emotional blackmail to get her own way, and why? To tell me my dad, who has never been my dad, wishes to see me and expects me to go and see him like He-Who-Must-Be-Obeyed. Well sod him. I'm not interested in anything he has to say, *or am I?* Maybe I should get all this sorted today. When will I get another chance to have it out with him and I had to admit to myself I was in no mood to back down today.

Steeling myself I entered the welfare. It was virtually empty but sitting at the bar was a middle-aged couple with their back to me. Christ, I needed some dutch courage. Ordering a double whisky at the bar, I downed it in one. Glancing at the couple at the side of me at the bar I recognised Maureen immediately: she had not changed in all the years and they were both looking at me. The whisky had hit the back of my throat and made me cough.

"I think you may be waiting for me," I announced. My voice sounded rough from the effect of the drink.

"Danielle, Danielle, is that you?" I nodded the man speaking I did not recognise him as the man who took me out as a child.

I had erased his image from my memory. The man I was looking at was approximatly 5ft 7inches with thinning brown hair; he was slightly overweight too but I did recognise the twinkle in his eye. He was beaming at me.

"Danielle, it is so good to see you. I can't believe you are here." Standing up he came up to me, wrapping me in his embrace. Flinching, I shuddered under his touch.

"Danielle, let's go somewhere a bit more private and talk."

He led us to the corner of the room well away from prying ears. "There's not been a day gone by that I have not thought about you."

His eyes were filling with tears. I felt numb; I knew this was my dad but I felt nothing for him, it was like meeting a stranger for the first time. Maureen was watching intently.

"Look, Dad what do you want? You have not bothered with me, so why are you bothering now?"

Frowning and looking hurt he reached his hand out to touch mine. "Danielle, no. You have got it all wrong. I came to see you when you were younger and took you out a few times, don't you remember?"

Remember? The very words made me shudder at the memory of me shivering in the cold waiting for him.

"Don't make me laugh. OK, yes, I have seen you, what, three times in my entire life, but you soon got bored with that, and decided to not show up on your last visit. Don't give me all this sentimental crap."

Shaking his head he said, "No, no, you have it all wrong. I was there when you were born, Danielle, your mum and I split up when you were around eighteen months old. I don't want to speak ill of your mother but it was her doing she was messing around on me. I left, leaving her and you in the house. Maureen and I met after all this and got married a few years after; your mum started moving around a lot after that and I lost contact with both of you. I finally tracked you down when she had married Jerry and I loved taking you out and was heartbroken when your mum stopped me seeing you. That's why I left my phone number so you could contact me."

I was hearing him but the words weren't going in I needed answers. "So where was I born?"

"Seventh Avenue, Clipstone. You are the only one I have got, and you were born at home."

"What do you mean my mum stopped you seeing me?"

"Well I went to collect you as arranged but your mum said your stepdad was giving you a hard time for seeing me, so asked me to stay away."

Damn her. So she had stopped me seeing my dad and lied about everything, but then again how could I believe him? He was a stranger to me, a stranger who had hurt me in the past. "OK then, Dad answer this. Yes you did give me your number, but then the following week you were meant to take me out but never showed."

"No what makes you think that? I was told to keep away I would never not show up if I had arranged to see you."

Reality hit me, hit me like a ton of bricks. "Sorry I need to go, I can't be here right now."

My dad was scribbling on a piece of paper. "Here take this. I never changed my number. Never changed it, just in case one day you would call."

My hand was shaking as I took the paper.

"Please call Danielle." Promising I would, I left.

38

I felt physically sick. I was not sure if it was from the effects of the whisky I had downed, the shock revelation that my whole life, or what I believed was my life, was a lie, a lie concocted by my mum. Everything I believed about myself was a lie: so I was never born in a mental hospital, my mum had never had a breakdown, my dad had never had an affair and left us for Maureen and her kids. He had wanted to see me, but my mum had stopped him and then made me sit outside waiting for him, knowing he would never show.

Why on earth would she say all this? Do all this to someone she was meant to love, make up such crazy lies? Was it a control thing? Was she on some kind of crazed power trip? She had been while I was growing up my main carer, after all there had been no one else. I needed to think, well try and think. There were so many questions and yet I did not know what to believe or who to believe. That night I tossed and turned in bed, trying to make sense of this new revelation, but no matter how hard I tried to rationalise it all I was incapable of believing my mother was such a cruel fake.

What if my dad was lying to make himself seem the injured party, to look better in my eyes. I needed someone to talk to, someone who knew both my mum and dad and who would be unbiased and who knew them from the start, I needed my grandma.

The next morning, throwing a few essentials into a case, I caught the National Express coach to Newcastle Upon Tyne. I had called ahead and though my grandma sounded surprised to hear from me after so long she was excited I was going to see her. The journey up was reminicent of the many journeys I had taken with my mother while I was younger, and I had to keep swallowing hard to stop the tears forming as I remembered the packed lunches she had made and the small talk we used to have on our trip up.

I was kind of hoping that my grandma would dismiss what my dad had said and back up my mum's story, but deep down I already knew the outcome, and it made me sick to think my own mother could do this to me her own daughter, her only child. On arriving at my auntie's house where my grandma was now living since my grandad had passed away, I nervously rang the doorbell. After what felt a lifetime my grandma opened the door.

"Danielle, come in. My, haven't you grown."

Stepping into the hallway I followed her into the lounge. "I bet you're ready for a drink after your journey, I will put the kettle on and then we can have a catch up, hinny."

Handing me the steaming cup of tea, we settled

ourselves on the cream leather settee. My aunt's house was immaculate; they had lived in the same house since they were married and over the years made endless improvements.

"Well I must admit it's nice to see you, is there a particular reason for the visit?"

Blushing I struggled to find the words – how was I going to explain this to her?

Looking at my grandma sitting opposite me, she looked so weak and fragile, a shadow of her former self. How the hell was I going to approach this? She was sat looking at me all expectantly.

"Grandma, how are you? Are you enjoying living here?"

"I am well thanks, getting older as you do, but happy and I love being here. I have my own space, but have people here if I need them."

I could see in her face it was all genuine she was beaming.

"I am so pleased for you, Gran, I would hate for you to be lonely."

"I'm fine, you don't need to worry about me, but more importantly how are you? You look tired, Danielle, and your mum, how is she?" The look I shot at her at the mere mention of my mother's name; gave the game away. "Oh no what's happened?"

Taking a deep breath and without going into too much detail I explained how my dad had got back in touch after all these years.

My grandma looked surprised and taken aback. "I often wondered why you never mentioned your dad. He was not really what I would have wanted for your mum, I had nothing against him, it was just he was in the army working abroad when they met, and I always feared he would be killed or take her away. I was surprised when they split. You were so young at the time; we tried to convince her to move back so we could be there for her, but your mum was having none of it."

So there it was. The truth as I had expected was out; my whole life had been a crazy lie concocted by my so-called mother.

"Gran, can you remember where I was born? And how old I was when he left?"

"At home. Everyone had their babies at home in those days. And I don't honestly remember how old you were, but you were either crawling or toddling, it was a long time ago, Danielle."

So there it all was, the clarification I needed to confirm my dad's story and blow my mother's to kingdom come. "So what are you going to do, are you going to see him? I bet you have a load of questions you need answering."

Sighing, I shrugged. "To be honest, I don't know right now"

"I know it's difficult but I think you should give him a chance. From what I can remember he doted on you, it's such a shame you lost contact."

I could feel myself starting to well up so quickly changed the subject to more mundane things. "If it's OK with you. I will stay tomorrow and travel back Wednesday. It would be nice to have a catch up with my relatives while I am here."

39

On the return journey home I was livid, livid that my mother had the ability to turn my world upside down and affect me the way she did. That she could use my grandma, a sweet, fragile old lady, making out she was ill to get control over me as she knew it was the only way I would have acknowledged her. Depriving me of the relationship I could have had, and should have had with my father, for having to put up with her neglect and mental and emotional abuse. For the torment she had caused me and the emotional scars I would probably never heal from.

I was having her, as soon as I got back I was going round and giving her what for. The coach was pulling into a service station for a toilet stop etc, and I was cursing the driver just itching to get back. My grandma had packed me a lunch but I had not touched it as my stomach was in knots and I could not stomach it. She had also got me a magazine for the journey back. My head was to full to take any of the information in, but it was looking pretty tattered and worn where I had been twisting it round and round in sheer frustration.

It was dark when the coach pulled into the Mansfield bus station. Jumping off I ran to the stop where the bus pulled in to take me to my mother's. Checking the time table, the next bus was due in around half an hour. Damn, I hated these evening buses. Pacing the bus station, cursing under my breath, I had no choice but to wait. My head was spinning with what I was going to say. I had worked it out exactly for the best effect so I just had to hold my nerve and do it. Finally the bus pulled in, I could feel myself hesitating – did I really want to confront her? Was I strong enough to go through with it. Sitting down I watched the passengers depart the bus, there was no one else waiting to get on so it was now or never. The driver seeing me watching him, smiled and beckoned me forward. Passing him my fare my hands were shaking and I fumbled to pick up my change from the tray. Taking my seat I cursed myself for being so weak, but I had never had a voice, never been allowed to speak up for myself, I had been downtrodden and put down for as long as I could remember, so no wonder I was petrified facing my persecutor.

Walking up the drive, the living room light was on. I could see through the window that she was sat in her usual place a book in hand and a bottle and glass at the side of her. Not knocking, I walked straight in. The dog, curled up in his basket, jumped up, tail wagging to greet me. Looking up from her book, surprised to see me, she smiled, "Danielle,

I have been so worried about you. How did it go with your dad? Sit down and tell me all about it."

"I'm not here on a social visit, so no I won't be sitting down, and yes I did see my dad. In fact it was quite an eye-opener."

Looking visibly shaken my mother stood up. "I don't understand, why, what happened?" she asked.

"Don't give me all this false sympathy. The game's up; I know everything. I know all the lies you concocted, all about the poison you fed me as a child about my dad. You're sick, sick in the head."

"Look, Danielle, I don't know what rubbish your dad has been telling you but I can assure you, I never lied to you."

Putting my head back, laughing, mocking her I said, "There you go again. You can't help yourself, even when your bang to rights you keep digging. My dad's told me the truth and I have had it confirmed. You stopped me seeing him, even told me he was dead and you're trying to tell me that's normal."

Tears were welling up in my mum's eyes but I was not giving an inch. The times I had cried, too scared and ashamed to speak to anyone. "I am done with you, done with you and your sick fantasies."

Walking towards me she had her arms outstretched to me, "Please, Danielle, I was only thinking of you. He was never bothered about you, I was protecting you from the truth." she was inches away from my face but I was not backing down.

"The truth? You wouldn't know the truth if it hit you in the face."

"Danielle, he's not your dad, that's why I kept you away."

I could take no more of this. "STOP! Stop with your malicious lies. I don't want to hear them anymore."

Turning away from her she grabbed my wrist. "NO, you must listen. It's the truth."

Her touch sickened me I wanted her nowhere near me, "Get off me!" Pulling my hand away she went to grab me again. Pushing her away from me she staggered backwards, losing her balance and went crashing through the glass-top table she had her drink placed on.

The sound of the breaking glass was ear-shattering, and she had landed on the floor with an almighty thud. She was not moving. Standing there looking at her, I felt nothing, no remorse just empty. The dog had come running in and was walking through all the fragments of glass; my first concern was picking him up so he didn't get cut. What was I going to do? Do the logical thing and call an ambulance, leave? After all no one is here, who would be any the wiser? After all it's not like I owed her anything. Yes, sod her, she can rot for all I cared. If Ryan came back he would figure she got wasted as usual, and fell when drunk.

Making sure I covered my tracks of being in the house, I let the dog out for a wee, filled his bowls up, ensured he was unable to get in the lounge and left. I must have made it a hundred yards down the street before turning back, my conscience getting the better of me. No I couldn't leave her like that. Damn her, I hated this hold she had over me. Ringing 999 I sat and waited for the inevitable: she had got her power back.

The story continues in the next book:

WHEN!!!